STAAR
Grade 5 Math Practice

GET DIGITAL ACCESS TO

 2 STAAR Tests

 Personalized Study Plans

REGISTER NOW

Link	QR Code

Visit the link below for online registration

lumoslearning.com/a/tedbooks

Access Code: G5MSTAAR-98265-P

State of Texas Assessments of Academic Readiness (STAAR) Test Practice: 5th Grade Math Practice Workbook and Full-length Online Assessments: Texas Test Study Guide

Contributing Editor - April LoTempio
Executive Producer - Mukunda Krishnaswamy
Program Director - Anirudh Agarwal
Designer and Illustrator - Snehal Sharan

ISBN 10: 1949855244

ISBN 13: 978-1949855241

Printed in the United States of America

FOR SCHOOL EDITION AND PERMISSIONS, CONTACT US

LUMOS INFORMATION SERVICES, LLC

 PO Box 1575, Piscataway, NJ 08855-1575
 www.LumosLearning.com

 Email: support@lumoslearning.com
 Tel: (732) 384-0146
 Fax: (866) 283-6471

Lumos Learning
Step Up Your Skills

INTRODUCTION

This book is specifically designed to improve student achievement on the State of Texas Assessment of Academic Readiness (STAAR). Students perform at their best on standardized tests when they feel comfortable with the test content as well as the test format. Lumos online practice tests are meticulously designed to mirror the state assessment. They adhere to the guidelines provided by the state for the number of sessions and questions, standards, difficulty level, question types, test duration and more.

Based on our decade of experience developing practice resources for standardized tests, we've created a dynamic system, the Lumos Smart Test Prep Methodology. It provides students with realistic assessment rehearsal and an efficient pathway to overcoming each proficiency gap.

Use the Lumos Smart Test Prep Methodology to achieve a high score on the STAAR.

Lumos Smart Test Prep Methodology

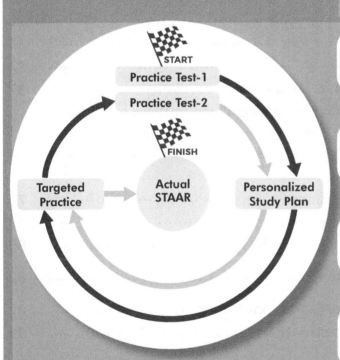

1 The student takes the first online diagnostic test, which assesses proficiency levels in various standards.

2 StepUp generates a personalized online study plan based on the student's performance.

3 The student completes targeted practice in the printed workbook and marks it as complete in the online study plan.

4 The student then attempts the second online practice test.

5 StepUp generates a second individualized online study plan.

6 The student completes the targeted practice and is ready for the actual STAAR

Table of Contents

Introduction ··· 1

Chapter 1 Numerical Representations and Relationships ····················· 4
Lesson 1   5.2 (A)   Read and write decimals ····································· 5
Lesson 2   5.2 (B)   Comparing and Ordering Decimals ····················· 7
Lesson 3   5.2 (C)   Rounding Decimals ··· 9
Lesson 4   5.3 (A)   Record and interpret calculations with numbers ····· 11
Lesson 5   5.3 (B)   Multiplication of whole numbers ····················· 13
Lesson 6   5.3 (C)   Division of whole numbers ······························· 16
Lesson 7   5.3 (D)
            5.3 (E)   Multiply Decimals ·· 18
Lesson 8   5.3 (F)
            5.3 (G)   Divide Decimals ··· 20
Lesson 9   5.3 (H)   Add & Subtract Fractions ··································· 22
Lesson 10   5.3 (H)   Problem Solving with Fractions ························· 25
Lesson 11   5.3 (I)   Multiply Fractions ··· 28
Lesson 12   5.3 (I)   Real world problems with Fractions ··················· 31
Lesson 13   5.3 (J)   Dividing by unit fractions ································· 34
Lesson 14   5.3 (K)   Rational Numbers, Addition & Subtraction ·········· 37
Lesson 15   5.3 (L)   Divide whole numbers by unit fractions and unit fractions by whole
                       numbers. ·· 41
                       Answer Key & Detailed Explanations ························ 44

Chapter 2 Computations and Algebraic Relationships ························· 76
Lesson 1   5.4 (A)   Identify prime and composite numbers ··············· 77
Lesson 2   5.4 (B)   Solve multi-step problems involving the four operations ········· 80
Lesson 3   5.4 (C)
            5.4 (D)   Analyze patterns and relationships ··················· 82
Lesson 4   5.4 (E)   Write & Interpret Numerical Expressions & Patterns ······· 87
                       Answer Key & Detailed Explanations ························ 89

Chapter 3 **Geometry & Measurement** ···································· **97**
Lesson 1 5.4 (G) Real world problems with volume ···················· 98
Lesson 2 5.4 (H) Perimeter & Area ·································· 101
Lesson 3 5.6 (A) Volume and Cubic Units ······················· 104
Lesson 4 5.6 (B) Volume of a rectangular prism ················· 107
Lesson 5 5.8 (A) Coordinate Geometry and Graphing Ordered Pairs of Numbers ······ 111
Lesson 6 5.8 (C) Real world graphing problems ·················· 116
Answer Key & Detailed Explanations ················· **121**

Chapter 4 **Data Analysis** ·· **128**
Lesson 1 5.9 (A)
5.9 (C) Representing and Interpreting Data ················· 129
Lesson 2 5.9 (B) Interpreting Data Tables & Scatter Plots ··············· 135
Answer Key & Detailed Explanations ················· **139**

Additional Information ··· **143**
Test Taking Tips and FAQs································ 143
What if I buy more than one Lumos tedBook? ················· 144
Progress Chart ·· 145

Chapter 1

Numerical Representations and Relationships

Chapter 1

Lesson 1: Read and Write Decimals

1. How is the number four hundredths written?

2. How is the number 0.2 read?

- Ⓐ Zero and two
- Ⓑ Decimal two
- Ⓒ Two tenths
- Ⓓ Two hundredths

3. What is the decimal form of $\frac{7}{10}$?

4. The number 0.05 can be represented by which fraction?

- Ⓐ $\frac{0}{5}$
- Ⓑ $\frac{5}{100}$
- Ⓒ $\frac{5}{10}$
- Ⓓ $\frac{1}{05}$

5. Which of the following numbers is equivalent to one half?

- Ⓐ 0.2
- Ⓑ 0.12
- Ⓒ 1.2
- Ⓓ 0.5

6. How is the number sixty three hundredths written?

7. What is the correct way to read the number 40.057?

Ⓐ Forty point five seven
Ⓑ Forty and fifty-seven hundredths
Ⓒ Forty and fifty-seven thousandths
Ⓓ Forty and five hundredths and seven thousandths

8. Which of the following numbers has:

0 in the hundredths place
8 in the tenths place
3 in the thousandths place
9 in the ones place

Ⓐ 9.083
Ⓑ 0.839
Ⓒ 9.803
Ⓓ 0.9803

9. For which number is this the expanded form?

$9 \times 10 + 2 \times 1 + 3 \times (\frac{1}{10}) + 8 \times (\frac{1}{100})$

Ⓐ 98.08
Ⓑ 93.48
Ⓒ 9.238
Ⓓ 92.38

10. What is the correct expanded form of the number 0.85?

Ⓐ $(8 \times 10) + (5 \times 100)$
Ⓑ $8 \times (\frac{1}{10}) + 5 \times (\frac{1}{100})$
Ⓒ $85 \div 10$
Ⓓ $(8 \div 10) \times (5 \div 10)$

Chapter 1

Lesson 2: Comparing and Ordering Decimals

1. Which of the following numbers is the least?
   0.04, 4.00, 0.40, 40.0

   Ⓐ 0.04
   Ⓑ 4.00
   Ⓒ 0.40
   Ⓓ 40.0

2. Which of the following numbers is greatest?
   0.125, 0.251, 0.512, 0.215

   Ⓐ 0.125
   Ⓑ 0.251
   Ⓒ 0.512
   Ⓓ 0.215

3. Which of the following numbers are greater than seven hundredths?

   Ⓐ 0.072
   Ⓑ 0.60
   Ⓒ 0.058
   Ⓓ 0.03

4. Which of the following comparisons are not correct?

   Ⓐ 48.01 = 48.1
   Ⓑ 25.4 < 25.40
   Ⓒ 10.83 < 10.093
   Ⓓ 392.01 < 392.1

5. Arrange these numbers in order from least to greatest:
   1.02, 1.2, 1.12, 2.12

   Ⓐ 1.2, 1.12, 1.02, 2.12
   Ⓑ 2.12, 1.2, 1.12, 1.02
   Ⓒ 1.02, 1.12, 1.2, 2.12
   Ⓓ 1.12, 2.12, 1.02, 1.2

6. Which of the following are false?

   Ⓐ 3.21 > 32.1
   Ⓑ 32.12 > 312.12
   Ⓒ 32.12 > 3.212
   Ⓓ 212.3 < 21.32

7. Arrange these numbers in order from greatest to least:
   2.4, 2.04, 2.21, 2.20

   Ⓐ 2.4, 2.04, 2.21, 2.20
   Ⓑ 2.4, 2.21, 2.20, 2.04
   Ⓒ 2.21, 2.20, 2.4, 2.04
   Ⓓ 2.20, 2.4, 2.04, 2.21

8. Which of the following comparisons is true?

   Ⓐ 0.403 > 0.304
   Ⓑ 0.043 < 0.403
   Ⓒ 0.043 < 0.304
   Ⓓ All of the above

9. Which number completes the following sequence?
   2.038, 2.039, _____

   Ⓐ 2.049
   Ⓑ 2.400
   Ⓒ 2.0391
   Ⓓ 2.04

10. Which of the following decimals is greater than 0.424 but less than 0.43?

   Ⓐ 0.4
   Ⓑ 0.423
   Ⓒ 0.431
   Ⓓ 0.429

Chapter 1

Lesson 3: Rounding Decimals

1. Is $7.48 closest to $6, $7 or $8?

Ⓐ $6
Ⓑ $7
Ⓒ $8
Ⓓ It is right in the middle of $7 and $8

2. Round the Olympic time of 56.389 seconds to the nearest tenth of a second.

3. Round the number 57.81492 to the nearest hundredth.

4. Which of the following numbers would round to 13.75?

Ⓐ 13.755
Ⓑ 13.70
Ⓒ 13.756
Ⓓ 13.747

5. Jerry spent $5.91, $7.27, and $12.60 on breakfast, lunch, and dinner. Approximately how much did his meals cost in all?

Ⓐ about $24
Ⓑ about $26
Ⓒ about $25
Ⓓ about $27

6. When rounding to the nearest one's place, which of the following results in 430?
   More than one option may be correct. Select all the correct answers.

   (A) 429.67
   (B) 430.49
   (C) 429.365
   (D) 430.05

7. Mika has a rectangular flower garden. It measures 12.2 meters on one side and 7.8 meters on the other. What is a reasonable estimation of the area of the flower garden? (Area= length x width)

   (A) 96 square meters
   (B) 20 square meters
   (C) 66 square meters
   (D) 120 square meters

8. Shanda ran a lap in 6.78 minutes. Assuming she maintains this time for every lap she runs, estimate the time it would take her to run three laps.

   (A) 25 minutes
   (B) 21 minutes
   (C) 18 minutes
   (D) 10 minutes

9. A basketball player scores an average of 13.2 points per game. During a 62-game season, he would be expected to score about _____ points. (Assume he will play every game.)

   (A) 600 points
   (B) 1,000 points
   (C) 800 points
   (D) 400 points

10. Use estimation to complete the following:
    The difference of 31.245 - 1.396 is between _____.

    (A) 29 and 29.5
    (B) 29.5 and 30
    (C) 30 and 30.5
    (D) 30.5 and 31

Lesson 4: Record and Interpret Calculations with Numbers

1. **Which expression shows 10 more than the quotient of 72 divided by 8?**

   Ⓐ $(10 + 72) \div 8$
   Ⓑ $(72 \div 8) + 10$
   Ⓒ $72 \div (8 + 10)$
   Ⓓ $8 \div (72 + 10)$

2. **Which expression shows 75 minus the product of 12 and 4?**

   Ⓐ $(75 - 12) \times 4$
   Ⓑ $(12 \times 4) - 75$
   Ⓒ $75 - (12 + 4)$
   Ⓓ $75 - (12 \times 4)$

3. **Jamie purchased 10 cases of soda for a party. Each case holds 24 cans. He also purchased 3 packs of juice. Each pack of juice has 6 cans. Which expression represents the number of cans he purchased?**

   Ⓐ $(10 \times 24) + (3 \times 6)$
   Ⓑ $(10 + 24) \times (3 + 6)$
   Ⓒ $10 \times (24 + 6)$
   Ⓓ $10 \times 24 \times 3 \times 6$

4. **Olivia had 42 pieces of candy. She kept 9 pieces for herself and then divided the rest evenly among her three friends. Which expression best represents the number of candy each friend received?**

   Ⓐ $(42 \div 3) - 9$
   Ⓑ $(42 - 9) \div 3$
   Ⓒ $42 \div (9 - 3)$
   Ⓓ $42 - (9 \div 3)$

5. **Which of the following options are true about the solution to 8 x (467 + 509)?**

   Ⓐ It is a number in the ten thousands.
   Ⓑ It is an even number.
   Ⓒ It is eight times the sum of 467 and 509.
   Ⓓ It is 509 more than the product of 8 and 467.

6. **Which of the following options are false about the solution to (3,259 – 741) ÷ 3?**

   Ⓐ It is one third as much as the difference of 3,259 and 741.
   Ⓑ It is 741 less than the quotient of 3,259 divided by 3.
   Ⓒ It is a whole number.
   Ⓓ It is a number in the thousands.

7. **Which of these expressions would result in the greatest number?**

   Ⓐ 420 – (28 x 13)
   Ⓑ 420 + 28 + 13
   Ⓒ (420 – 28) x 13
   Ⓓ 420 + (28 x 13)

8. **Which of these expressions would result in the smallest number?**

   Ⓐ 684 – (47 + 6)
   Ⓑ 684 – 47 – 6
   Ⓒ (684 – 47) x 6
   Ⓓ 684 – (47 x 6)

9. **Each of the 25 students in a class sold 7 items for a fundraiser. Their teacher also sold 13 items. Which expression best represents the number of items they sold in all?**

   Ⓐ 25 x (7 + 13)
   Ⓑ 13 + (25 x 7)
   Ⓒ 7 x (25 + 13)
   Ⓓ 25 + 7 + 13

10. **Mario had $75. He doubled that amount by mowing his neighbor's lawn all summer. Then he spent $47 on new sneakers. Which expression best represents the amount of money he now has?**

   Ⓐ (75 x 2) - 47
   Ⓑ (75 + 75) ÷ 47
   Ⓒ 47 – (75 + 2)
   Ⓓ 75 + 2 - 47

Chapter 1

Lesson 5: Multiplication of Whole Numbers

1. Solve 79 x 14 = _____

2. A farmer plants 18 rows of beans. If there are 50 bean plants in each row, how many plants will he have altogether?

3. Solve 680 x 94 = _____

   Ⓐ 64,070
   Ⓑ 63,960
   Ⓒ 64,760
   Ⓓ 63,920

4. What is the missing value?
   ____ x 11 = 374

5. Which of the following statements is true?

   Ⓐ 28 x 17 = 17 x 28
   Ⓑ 28 x 17 = 20 x 8 x 10 x 7
   Ⓒ 28 x 17 = (28 x 1) + (28 x 7)
   Ⓓ 28 x 17 = 27 x 18

6. Which equation is represented by this array?

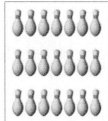

- Ⓐ 3 + 7 + 3 + 7 = 20
- Ⓑ 7 + 7 + 7 + 7 + 7 = 35
- Ⓒ 3 x 3 + 7 = 16
- Ⓓ 3 x 7 = 21

7. What would be a quick way to solve 596 x 101 accurately?

- Ⓐ Multiply 5 x 101, 9 x 101, 6 x 101, then add the products.
- Ⓑ Multiply 596 x 100 then add 596 more.
- Ⓒ Shift the 1 and multiply 597 x 100 instead.
- Ⓓ Estimate 600 x 100.

8. Harold baked 9 trays of cookies for a party. Three of the trays held 15 cookies each and six of the trays held 18 cookies each. How many cookies did Harold bake in all?

- Ⓐ 297
- Ⓑ 135
- Ⓒ 153
- Ⓓ 162

9. What's wrong with the following computation?

```
      2 8
    x 5 3
    -------
      3 2
      6 0
    4 0 0
+ 1 0 0 0
  ---------
  1 4 9 2
```

- Ⓐ 3 x 8 is multiplied incorrectly.
- Ⓑ 50 x 20 should only have two zeros.
- Ⓒ 5 x 8 is only 40.
- Ⓓ There's a missing 1 that should have been carried from the tens to the hundreds place.

10. Solve

407 x 35 = _____

Ⓐ 14,280
Ⓑ 14,245
Ⓒ 12,445
Ⓓ 16,135

Chapter 1

Lesson 6: Division of Whole Numbers

1. Find the missing number:
   48 ÷ ___ = 12

2. Hannah is filling gift bags for a party. She has 72 pieces of candy to distribute. If there are 8 bags, how many pieces of candy will go in each bag?

   Ⓐ 8
   Ⓑ 10
   Ⓒ 9
   Ⓓ 7

3. Solve 1,248 ÷ 6 =

4. The fifth grade class took a field trip to the theater. The 96 students sat in rows with 10 students in each row. How many rows did they use?

   Ⓐ 11
   Ⓑ 9
   Ⓒ 10
   Ⓓ 12

5. What is the value of 6,720 ÷ 15?

6. What is 675,000 divided by 100?

Ⓐ 675
Ⓑ 67,500
Ⓒ 67.5
Ⓓ 6,750

7. Which of the following statements is true?

Ⓐ $75 \div 0 = 0$
Ⓑ $75 \div 0 = 1$
Ⓒ $75 \div 0 = 75$
Ⓓ $75 \div 0$ cannot be solved

8. Taylor is putting 100 donuts into boxes. Each box holds 12 donuts. How many donuts will be left over after filling the last box fully?

Ⓐ 4
Ⓑ 8
Ⓒ 9
Ⓓ 5

9. Which of the following statements is true?

Ⓐ $26 \div 1 = 1$
Ⓑ $26 \div 1 = 26$
Ⓒ $26 \div 1 = 0$
Ⓓ $26 \div 1$ cannot be solved

10. Jeremy is rolling coins to take to the bank. He has 680 nickels to roll. If each sleeve holds 40 nickels, how many sleeves will he be able to fill?

Ⓐ 8
Ⓑ 17
Ⓒ 16
Ⓓ 12

Chapter 1

Lesson 7: Multiply Decimals

1. A stamp costs $0.42. How much money would you need to buy 8 stamps?

Ⓐ $.82
Ⓑ $3.33
Ⓒ $3.36
Ⓓ $4.52

2. Find the product:
   0.25 x 1.1 =

3. Find the product of 0.3 and 4.

4. Multiply:
   3 x 0.6 =

5. Multiply:
   0.12 x 12 =

Ⓐ 144
Ⓑ 14.4
Ⓒ 1.44
Ⓓ 24

6. Find the product of 25 and 0.3.

Ⓐ 75
Ⓑ .75
Ⓒ 7.5
Ⓓ 125

7. Sheila bought five pencils for $0.35 each. How much, before tax, will her total be?

Ⓐ $0.25
Ⓑ $0.75
Ⓒ $2.25
Ⓓ $1.75

8. Multiply:
1.4 x 0.7 =

Ⓐ 1.7
Ⓑ 1.4
Ⓒ 9.80
Ⓓ 0.98

9. Multiply:
3 x 0.5 =

Ⓐ 15
Ⓑ 1.50
Ⓒ 0.15
Ⓓ 15.15

10. Find the product of 1.5 and 0.5.

Ⓐ 0.75
Ⓑ 0.7
Ⓒ 0.50
Ⓓ 1.5

Chapter 1

Lesson 8: Divide Decimals

1. Divide 0.42 by 3.

2. Solve:
   0.09 ÷ 0.3 =

3. For Shanna's dress she needs to cut a ribbon in half. The ribbon is 4.8 meters. If she cuts the ribbon in half correctly, how long will each ribbon be?

   Ⓐ 2.4 meters
   Ⓑ 24 meters
   Ⓒ 0.24 meters
   Ⓓ 2 meters

4. Divide 0.15 by 3.

5. Divide:
   0.52 ÷ 4

   Ⓐ 0.13
   Ⓑ 13
   Ⓒ 130
   Ⓓ 0.1013

6. Divide 3.6 by 6.

Ⓐ 36
Ⓑ 0.36
Ⓒ 60
Ⓓ 0.6

7. Find the quotient:
$0.6 \div 4 =$

Ⓐ 0.15
Ⓑ 15
Ⓒ 1.5
Ⓓ 15.5

8. Find the quotient:
$0.12 \div 5 =$

Ⓐ 24
Ⓑ 52
Ⓒ 0.024
Ⓓ 48

9. What is $9.08 \div 4$?

Ⓐ 0.102
Ⓑ 0.227
Ⓒ 2.27
Ⓓ 21.02

10. Divide:
$0.24 \div 6 =$

Ⓐ 1.44
Ⓑ 0.04
Ⓒ 0.4
Ⓓ 5.8

Chapter 1

Lesson 9: Add & Subtract Fractions

1. Add: $\dfrac{2}{10} + \dfrac{1}{10} =$ Write your answer in reduced form.

2. To make a bowl of punch, Joe mixed $1\dfrac{1}{4}$ gallons of juice with $1\dfrac{2}{4}$ gallons of sparkling water. How much punch does he have?

   Ⓐ $2\dfrac{3}{4}$ gallons

   Ⓑ 3 gallons

   Ⓒ $\dfrac{1}{4}$ gallon

   Ⓓ $\dfrac{3}{4}$ gallon

3. Subtract: $\dfrac{3}{4} - \dfrac{2}{4}$. Write your answer in reduced form.

4. Subtract: $3\dfrac{4}{10} - 1\dfrac{1}{10} =$

Ⓐ $1\dfrac{3}{10}$

Ⓑ $2\dfrac{1}{10}$

Ⓒ $3\dfrac{3}{10}$

Ⓓ $2\dfrac{3}{10}$

5. To add the fractions $\dfrac{3}{4}$ and $\dfrac{7}{12}$, what must first be done?

Ⓐ Reduce the fractions to lowest terms
Ⓑ Change to improper fractions
Ⓒ Make the numerators the same
Ⓓ Find a common denominator

6. Add: $\dfrac{1}{2} + \dfrac{1}{4} =$

Ⓐ $\dfrac{2}{6}$

Ⓑ $\dfrac{2}{3}$

Ⓒ $\dfrac{3}{4}$

Ⓓ $\dfrac{1}{2}$

7. Find the difference: $\dfrac{2}{3} - \dfrac{1}{9}$. Write your answer in reduced form.

8. Find the sum: $2\dfrac{1}{8} + 5\dfrac{1}{2} =$

   Ⓐ $7\dfrac{2}{10}$

   Ⓑ $10\dfrac{1}{16}$

   Ⓒ $3\dfrac{1}{6}$

   Ⓓ $7\dfrac{5}{8}$

9. Find the sum of five and five eighths plus one and one fourth.

   Ⓐ $6\dfrac{7}{8}$

   Ⓑ $10\dfrac{6}{8}$

   Ⓒ $6\dfrac{6}{12}$

   Ⓓ $7\dfrac{2}{10}$

10. Subtract: $5 - \dfrac{1}{3} =$

   Ⓐ $5\dfrac{1}{3}$

   Ⓑ $4\dfrac{1}{3}$

   Ⓒ $3\dfrac{2}{3}$

   Ⓓ $4\dfrac{2}{3}$

Chapter 1

Lesson 10: Problem Solving with Fractions

1. Susan's homework was to practice the piano for $\frac{3}{4}$ of an hour each night. How many minutes each night did she practice?

   Ⓐ 30 minutes
   Ⓑ 15 minutes
   Ⓒ 45 minutes
   Ⓓ 60 minutes

2. Three fifths of the 30 students are boys. How many students are girls?

3. Walking at a steady pace, Ella walked 11 miles in 3 hours. Which mixed number shows how many miles she walked in an hour?

   Ⓐ $\frac{2}{3}$
   Ⓑ $2\frac{2}{3}$
   Ⓒ 3
   Ⓓ $3\frac{2}{3}$

4. In science class we discovered that $\frac{7}{8}$ of an apple is water. What fraction of the apple is not water?

   Ⓐ $\frac{1}{6}$
   Ⓑ $\frac{1}{7}$
   Ⓒ $\frac{7}{8}$
   Ⓓ $\frac{1}{8}$

5. There were 20 pumpkins in a garden. One-fourth of the pumpkins were too small, one-tenth were too large, and one-half were just the right size. The rest were not ripe yet. How many of the pumpkins were too small?

6. Timothy decided to clean out his closet by donating some of his 45 button-down shirts. He gave away 9 shirts. What fraction of the shirts did he give away?

   (A) $\dfrac{1}{5}$

   (B) $\dfrac{1}{9}$

   (C) $\dfrac{1}{2}$

   (D) $\dfrac{36}{45}$

7. There are 32 students in Mr. Duffy's class. If 4 come to after school tutoring, what fraction of the class comes to after school tutoring?

   (A) $\dfrac{28}{32}$

   (B) $\dfrac{1}{8}$

   (C) $\dfrac{1}{4}$

   (D) $\dfrac{2}{8}$

8. Dara has to solve 35 math problems for homework. She has completed 14 of them. What fraction of the problems does she have left to do?

   (A) $\dfrac{14}{35}$

   (B) $\dfrac{3}{5}$

   (C) $\dfrac{14}{21}$

   (D) $\dfrac{2}{5}$

9. A 5th grade volleyball team scored 32 points in one game. Of those points, $\frac{2}{8}$ were scored in the second half. How many points were scored in the first half of the game?

10. A recipe to make 48 cookies calls for 3 cups of flour. However, you do not want to make 48 cookies, but only 24 cookies. Which fraction shows how much flour to use?

Ⓐ 2 cups

Ⓑ $1\frac{2}{3}$ cups

Ⓒ $1\frac{1}{2}$ cups

Ⓓ $2\frac{2}{3}$ cups

Chapter 1

Lesson 11: Multiply Fractions

1. Multiply: $\dfrac{2}{3} \times \dfrac{4}{5} =$

   Ⓐ $\dfrac{8}{15}$

   Ⓑ $\dfrac{3}{4}$

   Ⓒ $\dfrac{6}{8}$

   Ⓓ $\dfrac{4}{15}$

2. Find the product: $5 \times \dfrac{2}{3} \times \dfrac{1}{2} =$

   Ⓐ $1\dfrac{1}{3}$

   Ⓑ 5

   Ⓒ $2\dfrac{2}{3}$

   Ⓓ $1\dfrac{2}{3}$

3. Which of the following is equivalent to $\dfrac{5}{6} \times 7$?

   Ⓐ $5 \div (6 \times 7)$
   Ⓑ $(5 \times 7) \div 6$
   Ⓒ $(6 \times 7) \div 5$
   Ⓓ $(1 \div 7) \times (5 \div 6)$

4. Which of the following is equivalent to $\dfrac{4}{10} \times \dfrac{3}{8}$?

   Ⓐ $4 \div (10 \times 3) \div 8$
   Ⓑ $(4 + 3) \times (10 + 8)$
   Ⓒ $(4 \times 3) \div (10 \times 8)$
   Ⓓ $(4 - 3) \div (10 - 8)$

5. Hector is using wood to build a dog house. Each wall is $\frac{4}{7}$ of a yard tall and $\frac{3}{5}$ of a yard wide. Knowing that the area of each wall is the base times the height, how many square yards of wood will he need to build 4 walls of equal size?

Ⓐ $1\frac{2}{3}$

Ⓑ $1\frac{13}{35}$

Ⓒ $\frac{12}{35}$

Ⓓ $1\frac{4}{12}$

6. An auditorium has 600 seats. One-third of the seats are empty. How many seats are empty?

Ⓐ 300 seats
Ⓑ 400 seats
Ⓒ 200 seats
Ⓓ 900 seats

7. Which of these numbers is not equivalent to the other three?

Ⓐ $\frac{44}{8}$

Ⓑ $5\frac{25}{50}$

Ⓒ $5\frac{1}{5}$

Ⓓ 5.500

8. Multiply: $\frac{1}{2} \times \frac{1}{4} =$

9. What fraction is one half of three fourths?

10. One half of one tenth is what fraction?

Chapter 1

Lesson 12: Real World Problems with Fractions

1. Chef Chris is using $\frac{3}{4}$ lb. of chicken per person at a luncheon. If there are 17 people at the luncheon, how many pounds of chicken will he use?

   Ⓐ $12\frac{3}{4}$

   Ⓑ $\frac{51}{68}$

   Ⓒ $\frac{48}{4}$

   Ⓓ $17\frac{3}{4}$

2. A team of runners ran a relay race $\frac{9}{10}$ of a mile long. If Carl ran $\frac{3}{5}$ of the race, how far did his teammates run?

   Ⓐ $\frac{9}{25}$ mile

   Ⓑ $\frac{27}{50}$ mile

   Ⓒ $\frac{1}{10}$ mile

   Ⓓ $\frac{2}{5}$ mile

3. There are $1\frac{4}{5}$ pounds of jelly beans in each bag. If Mrs. Lancer buys 3 bags of jelly beans for her class, how many pounds of jelly beans will she have in all?

   Ⓐ $3\frac{12}{15}$

   Ⓑ $5\frac{2}{5}$

   Ⓒ $3\frac{4}{15}$

   Ⓓ $5\frac{4}{5}$

4. Mario is in a bike race that is $3\frac{1}{5}$ miles long. He gets a flat tire $\frac{2}{3}$ of the way into the race. How many miles did he make it before he got a flat tire?

   Ⓐ $3\frac{2}{15}$

   Ⓑ $1\frac{3}{8}$

   Ⓒ $2\frac{2}{15}$

   Ⓓ $\frac{2}{3}$

5. Jackson is swimming laps in a pool that is $20\frac{1}{2}$ meters long. He swims $4\frac{1}{2}$ laps. How many meters did he swim?

   Ⓐ $80\frac{1}{4}$

   Ⓑ $92\frac{1}{4}$

   Ⓒ $84\frac{1}{2}$

   Ⓓ 90

6. A sack of potatoes weighs $4\frac{2}{3}$ lbs. If there are 20 sacks of potatoes in a crate, what is the total weight of the potatoes (in pounds)?

   Ⓐ $93\frac{1}{3}$

   Ⓑ $80\frac{40}{60}$

   Ⓒ $80\frac{2}{3}$

   Ⓓ $24\frac{2}{3}$

7. A factory packages bolts that are each $1\frac{1}{8}$ inches wide. If there are 6 bolts side-by-side in a package, how many inches wide must the packaging be?

   Ⓐ $6\frac{1}{8}$

   Ⓑ $7\frac{5}{8}$

   Ⓒ $7\frac{1}{8}$

   Ⓓ $6\frac{6}{8}$

8. There are 21 students in a fifth grade class. It takes their teacher $1\frac{1}{4}$ hours to complete each student's report card. How many hours will the report cards take all together? Write your answer in the box below.

9. Kara multiplied some measurements to determine that she needs $\frac{14}{3}$ yards of fabric for a project. How many yards of fabric should she ask for at the store? Convert the given fraction to a mixed fraction?

10. Danny needs $5\frac{1}{4}$ feet of tile trim for his kitchen. The tile is sold in pieces that are $\frac{1}{4}$ of a foot long. How many pieces should he buy?

Chapter 1

Lesson 13: Dividing by unit fractions

1. Divide: $2 \div \dfrac{1}{3} =$

2. In order to divide by a fraction you must first:

   (A) find its reciprocal
   (B) match its denominator
   (C) find its factors
   (D) multiply by the numerator

3. Divide: $3 \div \dfrac{2}{3}$. Write your answer in mixed fraction form.

4. Complete the following:
   Dividing a number by a fraction less than 1 results in a quotient that is _____ the original number.

   (A) the reciprocal of
   (B) less than
   (C) greater than
   (D) equal to

5. 5 people want to evenly share a $\dfrac{1}{3}$ pound bag of peanuts. How many pounds should each person get?

Ⓐ $\dfrac{3}{5}$

Ⓑ $1\dfrac{2}{3}$

Ⓒ $\dfrac{3}{15}$

Ⓓ $\dfrac{1}{15}$

6. A jeweler has $\dfrac{1}{8}$ of a pound of gold. If she uses it to make 4 bracelets, how many pounds of gold will be in each bracelet?

Ⓐ $\dfrac{2}{16}$

Ⓑ $\dfrac{1}{32}$

Ⓒ $\dfrac{1}{4}$

Ⓓ $\dfrac{4}{8}$

7. Tony is running a long-distance race. If he stops for water every $\dfrac{1}{3}$ mile, how many times will he stop for water in a 10-mile race?

8. Which statement proves that $\dfrac{1}{6} \div 3 = \dfrac{1}{18}$?

Ⓐ $\dfrac{3}{18} = 6$

Ⓑ $\dfrac{1}{6} \times 3 = \dfrac{3}{6}$

Ⓒ $\dfrac{1}{18} \div 3 = \dfrac{1}{6}$

Ⓓ $\dfrac{1}{18} \times 3 = \dfrac{3}{18}$

9. The scout leader bought an 8-pound bag of trail mix. If he divides it into $\frac{1}{4}$ pound servings, how many servings will there be?

    Ⓐ 20
    Ⓑ 32
    Ⓒ 4
    Ⓓ 18

10. Which statement proves that $10 \div \frac{1}{4} = 40$?
    Circle the correct answer

    Ⓐ $\frac{1}{40} \times 10 = \frac{10}{40}$

    Ⓑ $\frac{1}{4} \times \frac{1}{10} = \frac{1}{40}$

    Ⓒ $40 \times \frac{1}{4} = 10$

    Ⓓ $4 \times 10 = 40$

Chapter 1

Lesson 14: Rational Numbers, Addition & Subtraction

1. Evaluate: 25 + 2.005 - 7.253 - 2.977

2. Add and/or subtract as indicated :  $-3\dfrac{4}{5} + 9\dfrac{7}{10} - 2\dfrac{11}{20} =$

  Ⓐ $3\dfrac{7}{20}$

  Ⓑ $4\dfrac{7}{10}$

  Ⓒ $4\dfrac{9}{20}$

  Ⓓ $3\dfrac{1}{20}$

3. Linda and Carrie made a trip from their hometown to a city about 200 miles away to attend a friend's wedding. The following chart shows their distances, stops and times. What part of their total trip did they spend driving?

3hr	driving
15 min	rest stop
1 1/2 hr	driving
1 hr	rest stop
20 min	driving

Ⓐ $\dfrac{4}{5}$

Ⓑ $\dfrac{2}{5}$

Ⓒ $\dfrac{58}{73}$

Ⓓ $\dfrac{99}{100}$

4. If $a = \dfrac{5}{6}$, $b = -\dfrac{2}{3}$ and $c = -1\dfrac{1}{3}$, find $a - b - c$.

Ⓐ $-1\dfrac{1}{6}$

Ⓑ $2\dfrac{5}{6}$

Ⓒ $-2\dfrac{1}{6}$

Ⓓ $-2\dfrac{5}{6}$

5. If Ralph ate half of his candy bar followed by half of the remainder followed by half of that remainder, what part was left?

Ⓐ $\dfrac{1}{4}$

Ⓑ $\dfrac{1}{8}$

Ⓒ $\dfrac{1}{6}$

Ⓓ $\dfrac{1}{3}$

6. Which expressions equal $-\dfrac{3}{4}$? Select all the correct answers.

Ⓐ $\dfrac{1}{8} - \dfrac{7}{8}$

Ⓑ $\dfrac{7}{8} - \dfrac{1}{8}$

Ⓒ $-\dfrac{6}{4} + \dfrac{3}{4}$

Ⓓ $\dfrac{1}{4} + \dfrac{1}{8}$

7. Ricky purchased shoes for $159.95 and then exchanged them at a buy 1, get 1 half off sale. The shoes that he purchased on his return trip were $74.99 and $68.55. How much did he receive back from the store after his second transaction?

Ⓐ $37.50

Ⓑ $68.55

Ⓒ $34.28

Ⓓ $50.68

8. Simplify the following expression:

$$3.24 - 1.914 - 6.025 + 9.86 - 2.2 + 5\frac{1}{2} =$$

- Ⓐ   -8.461
- Ⓑ   8.461
- Ⓒ   -11.259
- Ⓓ   11.259

9. John had $76.00. He gave Jim $42.45 and gave Todd $21.34. John will receive $14.50 later in the evening. How much money will John have later that night?

- Ⓐ $25.71
- Ⓑ $26.67
- Ⓒ $26.71
- Ⓓ $24.71

10. Jeri has had a savings account since she entered first grade. Each month of the first year she saved $1.00. Each month of the second year she saved $2.00 etc. until she completed ten years in which she saved $10.00 each month. How much has she saved at the end of ten years?

Chapter 1

Lesson 15: Divide whole numbers by unit fractions and unit fractions by whole numbers.

1. Which best explains why $6 \div \dfrac{1}{4} = 24$?

Ⓐ $24 \div \dfrac{1}{4} = 6$

Ⓑ $24 \times \dfrac{1}{4} = 6$

Ⓒ $24 \div 6 = \dfrac{1}{4}$

Ⓓ $24 = \dfrac{1}{4} \times 6$

2. Which model best represents the following equation?

$4 \div \dfrac{1}{3} = 12$

Ⓐ

Ⓑ

Ⓒ

Ⓓ

3. Which equation matches this model?

(A) $24 \div \dfrac{1}{8} = 3$

(B) $24 \div \dfrac{1}{3} = 8$

(C) $8 \div \dfrac{1}{3} = 24$

(D) $3 \div \dfrac{1}{8} = 24$

4. Byron has 5 pieces of wood from which to build his birdhouse. If he cuts each piece into fifths, how many pieces will he have?

(A) 25

(B) 5

(C) $\dfrac{1}{5}$

(D) $\dfrac{5}{25}$

5. Angelina has 10 yards of fabric. She needs $\dfrac{1}{3}$ yard of fabric for each purse she will sew. How many purses will she be able to make?

(A) $3\dfrac{1}{3}$

(B) $10\dfrac{1}{3}$

(C) 30

(D) 13

6. What is the value of 4 divided by $\dfrac{1}{5}$. Circle the correct answer choice.

(A) $\dfrac{4}{5}$

(B) 20

(C) $\dfrac{1}{20}$

(D) 9

7. Read each statement below and indicate whether it is true or false.

Statements	True	False
$\frac{1}{12} \div 4 > 40$	◯	◯
$\frac{1}{4} \div 7 = \frac{1}{14}$	◯	◯
$\frac{1}{3} \div 33 < 5$	◯	◯
$\frac{1}{8} \div 4 < \frac{1}{2}$	◯	◯

8. What three unit fractions complete the equations below? Enter your answers into the table.

	÷	14	=	$\frac{1}{112}$
	÷	29	=	$\frac{1}{87}$
	÷	55	=	$\frac{1}{495}$

9. Evaluate $8 \div \frac{1}{3}$.

Ⓐ 24
Ⓑ 27
Ⓒ 21
Ⓓ 2.7

10. Evaluate $4 \div \frac{7}{21}$.

Ⓐ 7
Ⓑ 12
Ⓒ 27
Ⓓ 36

End of Numerical Representations and Relationships

Answer Key and Detailed Explanations

Chapter 1:
Numerical Representations and Relationships

Lesson 1: Read and Write Decimals

Question No.	Answer	Detailed Explanations
1	0.04	The 4 goes in the hundredths place, which is two places to the right of the decimal. All other places get place-holder zeros.
2	C	The two is immediately to the right of the decimal, so it is in the tenths place. It is read "two tenths."
3	0.7	The fraction is seven tenths. To show this value in decimal form, use the digit 7 in the tenths place (immediately to the right of the decimal).
4	B	In the number 0.05, the 5 is in the hundredths place. To show this amount (five hundredths) as a fraction, use 5 as the numerator and 100 as the denominator.
5	D	One half is equal to five tenths (think of a pizza sliced into 10 pieces, half of the pizza would be 5 out of 10 slices). To show five tenths, use a 5 in the tenths place immediately to the right of the decimal.
6	0.63	Sixty hundredths is equivalent to six tenths (the place to the right of the decimal). Three hundredths is shown by a 3 in the hundredths place (two places to the right of the decimal).
7	C	Begin by saying the whole number (forty), the word 'and' for the decimal, and then the decimal portion of the number. The decimal .057 is fifty-seven thousandths. The 5 hundredths is equivalent to fifty thousandths.
8	C	The hundredths place (0) is two places to the right of the decimal. The tenths place (8) is immediately to the right of the decimal. The thousandths place (3) is three places to the right of the decimal. The ones place (9) is immediately to the left of the decimal.
9	D	In expanded form, each digit is multiplied by its place value and the products are added together. The expression $9 \times 10 + 2 \times 1 + 3 \times (\frac{1}{10}) + 8 \times (\frac{1}{100})$ can be thought of as: $9 \times 10 = 90$ $2 \times 1 = 2$ $3 \times (\frac{1}{10}) = .3$ $8 \times (\frac{1}{100}) = .08$ Add the products to get 92.38
10	B	In expanded form, each digit is multiplied by its place value and the products are added together. The number 0.85 is made up of 8 tenths, which is written as $8 \times (\frac{1}{10})$, and 5 hundredths, which is written as $5 \times (\frac{1}{100})$.

Lesson 2: Comparing & Ordering Decimals

Question No.	Answer	Detailed Explanations
1	A	Since each of the options contains only one non-zero digit (4), compare the place value of the 4 to find the lowest number. 0.04 is the lowest number because the 4 is the furthest to the right of the decimal (in the hundredths place).
2	C	In order to find the greatest number, compare the digit in the highest place value. All of the options have 0 ones, so look to the tenths place. The number with 5 in the tenths place is greater than the numbers with 1 or 2 in the tenths place, no matter what comes next.
3	A and B	Seven hundredths is written 0.07. In order for a number to be lower, it has to have 0 in the tenths place and a digit lower than 7 in the hundredths place.
4	A, B and C	Each of these options involves comparing decimals (since the numbers to the left of the decimal point in each option are equal). Remember, the further a number is to the right of a decimal, the lower its place value. Be sure to compare numbers that are in the same place value (compare tenths to tenths, etc.). For each of these options, compare the underlined digit: 48.01 = 48.1 These are not equal, because .0 is less than .1. 25.4 < 25.40 The final zero does not affect the number's value, so these two numbers are equal. 10.83 < 10.093 The 8 in the tenths place is greater than a 0 in the tenths place. 392.01 < 392.1. 1 is greater than .0.
5	C	In order to compare the size of numbers, begin with the place value furthest to the left. In this case, three of the numbers have a 1 in the ones place, so look to the tenths place to compare those three. The number with the lowest digit in the tenths place will come first (1.02) followed by the number with the next-highest digit in the tenths place (1.12) followed by the number with the highest digit in the tenths place (1.2). The remaining number has a 2 in the ones place, so it is the greatest.

Question No.	Answer	Detailed Explanations
6	A, B and D	Each of these options involves comparing similar digits in different place values. Be sure to compare numbers that are in the same place value (compare tenths to tenths, etc.), starting with the highest place value. For each of these options, compare the underlined digit: _3.21 > _32.1 - No tens is less than 3 tens. _32.12 > _312.12 - No hundreds is less than 3 hundreds. _32.12 > _3.212 - 3 tens is more than no tens. _212.3 < _21.32 - Two hundreds is greater than no hundreds.
7	B	In order to compare the size of numbers, begin with the place value furthest to the left. In this case, all of the numbers have a 2 in the ones place, so look to the tenths place to compare them. The number with the highest digit in the tenths place will come first (2._4_). The next two highest numbers both have a 2 in the tenths place, so look to the hundredths place. The number with the highest digit in the hundredths place will come first (2.2_1_) followed by the number with the lower digit in the hundredths place (2.2_0_). The final number has a 0 in the tenths place, so it is the least of all.
8	D	To compare these numbers, look at the digit in the highest place value (the tenths place). 0._4_03 is greater than 0._3_04 and 0._0_43, as it has 4 in tenths place and the other two numbers have 3 and 0 in the tenths place respectively. Therefore options (A) and (B) are correct. In Option (C), we are comparing 0._0_43 with 0._3_04. 0._3_04 has 3 in tenths place and 0._0_43 has 0 in tenths place. Since 0 < 3, 0.043 < 0.304. So, option (C) is also correct. So, option (D) is the correct answer.
9	D	This pattern is increasing by one thousandth every term. After 2.039, the thousandth place will increase by one. Since there is already a 9 in the thousandths place, it will become zero and the hundredths place will increase to 4. The number 2.040 can also be written 2.04.

Question No.	Answer	Detailed Explanations
10	D	When comparing decimals align the decimal places and add zeros to the end of any decimal so all numbers have the same number of decimal places. Then compare the numbers ignoring the decimal point. 0.424 = 0.424 0.43 = 0.430 0.4 = 0.400 0.423 = 0.423 0.431 = 0.431 0.429 = 0.429 Now that each number has three decimal places, order the numbers ignoring the decimals. 400, 423, 424, 429, 430, 431. The only number between 424 (0.424) and 430 (0.43) is 429. Thus the correct answer is 0.429.

Lesson 3: Rounding Decimals

Question No.	Answer	Detailed Explanations
1	B	In order to round to the nearest whole dollar, look to the tenths (dimes) place. In $7.48 there is a 4 in the tenths place, which means round down to $7.00.
2	56.4	In the number 56.389, there is a 3 in the tenths place. Look to the right to see that 8 means round up. The number becomes 56.4 with no hundredths or thousandths.
3	57.81	In the number 57.81492, there is a 1 in the hundredths place. To determine whether to round up to 2 or remain 1, look to the digit to the right. A 4 means that the number will round down to 57.81.
4	D	In order for a number to round to 13.75, it must be between 13.745 and 13.754. The number 13.747 has a 7 in the thousandths place that means it will round up to 13.75.
5	B	Round $5.91 up to $6. Round $7.27 down to $7. Round $12.60 up to $13. $6 + $7 + $13 = $26.
6	A,B & D	The correct answer choices are A, B and D. When rounding to the one's place, look at the tenths place. If the tenth's digit is 5 or more, round the one's place to the next digit and drop the decimal digits. If the tenth's place is less than 5, keep the one's digit and drop the decimal digits.

A. Since the tenth's digit is 6 the one's digit is rounded up and the decimal digits are dropped so that 429.67 becomes 430. This is a correct answer choice.

B. Since the tenth's digit is 4 the one's digit is kept and the decimal digits are dropped so that 430.49 becomes 430. This is a correct answer choice.

C. Since the tenth's digit is 3 the one's digit is kept and the decimal digits are dropped so that 429.365 becomes 429. This is an incorrect answer choice.

D. Since the tenth's digit is 0 the one's digit is kept and the decimal digits are dropped so that 430.05 becomes 430. This is a correct answer choice. |
| 7 | A | Round each measurement to the nearest whole number, then multiply. 12.2 rounds down to 12 (because of the 2 in the tenths place) and 7.8 rounds up to 8 (because of the 8 in the tenths place). 12 x 8 = 96. |
| 8 | B | Round 6.78 to the nearest whole number. Since there is a 7 in the tenths place, round up (to the whole number 7). 7 x 3 = 21. |

Question No.	Answer	Detailed Explanations
9	C	The answer options indicate that this problem can be solved using estimation. Round 13.2 down to 13 and 62 down to 60. 13 x 60 = 780, which is closest to the option '800 points.'
10	B	Round each number to the tenths place. 31.245 rounds down to 31.2 and 1.396 rounds up to 1.4. Think of 31.2 - 1.4 as 31.2 - 1.2 (which equals 30) minus another 0.2. That will put the answer slightly less than 30, so it is between 29.5 and 30.

Lesson 4: Record and Interpret Calculations with Numbers

Question No.	Answer	Detailed Explanations
1	B	First, find the quotient of 72 divided by 8 (72 ÷ 8). Then determine what ten more than that would be (+ 10).
2	D	First, find the product of 12 and 4 (12 x 4). Then subtract the product from 75.
3	A	Show 10 cases of 24 cans as (10 x 24) and 3 packs of six cans as (3 x 6). Add the two expressions to find the total: (10 x 24) + (3 x 6).
4	B	First, subtract the 9 that Olivia kept for herself (42 – 9). Then divide the difference among the three friends: (42 – 9) ÷ 3.
5	B and C	The expression 8 x (467 + 509) indicates that you should first find the sum of 467 and 509, and then multiply by 8. Therefore, the solution is 8 times the sum. Since the number is multiplied by 8, it will be even too.
6	B, C and D	The expression (3,259 – 741) ÷ 3 indicates that you should first find the difference of 3,259 and 741, and then divide by 3. Therefore, A is true. Other options are False.
7	C	A quick estimate shows that option C, a number in the hundreds times a number in the tens, would result in a number in the thousands. The other options would all result in a number in the hundreds.
8	D	A quick estimate shows that option D, in which the largest amount is subtracted from 684, would result in the smallest number. Options A and B subtract a relatively small amount from 684, and option C will actually result in a larger number.
9	B	First, multiply 7 items by the 25 students (25 x 7). Then add the 13 items sold by the teacher to this product 13 + (25 x 7).
10	A	First, double the $75 he had (75 x 2). Then subtract the $47 he spent: (75 x 2) - 47.

Lesson 5: Multiplication of Whole Numbers

Question No.	Answer	Detailed Explanations
1	1,106	<div align="center">79 x 1 4 ——— 3 6 2 8 0 9 0 + 7 0 0 ——— 1 1 0 6</div>
2	900	This is a multiplication problem, because it is an array of 18 rows with 50 objects in each row. <div align="center">5 0 x 1 8 ——— 0 4 0 0 0 + 5 0 0 ——— 9 0 0</div>
3	D	<div align="center">6 8 0 x 9 4 ——— 0 3 2 0 2 4 0 0 0 7 2 0 0 + 5 4 0 0 0 ——— 6 3,9 2 0</div>
4	34	Multiplying by 11 can be thought of as x 10 and x 1 more. 34 x 10 = 340 and 34 x 1 = 34. Together they equal 374. Alternate Method : We have to find the number, which, when multiplied with 11 gives 374. Number = 374/11. Use standard long division algorithm to find the number. Number = 34.

Question No.	Answer	Detailed Explanations
5	A	The Commutative Property of Multiplication states that when two factors are multiplied together, the product is the same no matter the order of the factors.
6	D	The array shows three rows with seven objects in each row. There are 21 objects in all. The array is called a 3 by 7 array, which is shown as $3 \times 7 = 21$.
7	B	According to the Distributive Property of Multiplication, you can break one of the factors (101) into two parts (100 and 1) and multiply them both by the other factor. 596×100 and 596×1 will produce the same answer as multiplying 596×100 and adding 596 more.
8	C	Three of the trays held 15 cookies each, so $3 \times 15 = 45$. The other six trays held 18 cookies each, so $6 \times 18 = 108$. To find the total, add $45 + 108 = 153$.
9	A	In the first step, 3×8 is recorded as 32. It should be 24.
10	B

```
    4 0 7
  x   3 5

      3 5
        0
  2 0 0 0
    2 1 0
        0
+ 1 2 0 0 0
_____
1 4,2 4 5
```
 |

Lesson 6: Division of Whole Numbers

Question No.	Answer	Detailed Explanations
1	4	The equation 48 ÷ ___ = 12 can be thought of as 48 ÷ 12 = ___. There are 4 twelves in 48. Check the work by using multiplication (4 x 12 = 48).
2	C	To solve the problem, divide 72 by 8. 72 can be divided evenly by 8. Check the work by using multiplication (8 x 9 = 72).
3	208	1248 divided by 6 is 208 with remainder 0 = 208 R 0 = 208 $\frac{0}{6}$ **Show Work:** 0 2 0 8 6⟌1 2 4 8 0 — 1 2 1 2 — 0 4 0 — 4 8 4 8 — 0
4	C	Divide the number of students by the number of seats in each row. 96 ÷ 10 = 9 R 6. The remaining 6 students still had to sit in a row, even though it was not full. The answer is 10 rows.
5	448	6720 divided by 15 is 448 with remainder 0 = 448 R 0 = 448 $\frac{0}{15}$ **Show Work:** 0 4 4 8 1 5⟌6 7 2 0 0 — 6 7 6 0 — 7 2 6 0 — 1 2 0 1 2 0 — 0

Question No.	Answer	Detailed Explanations
6	D	To divide by 100, move the decimal point two places to the left. When a whole number ending with zeros is the dividend, take off as many 0's as appear in the divisor from the dividend to get the quotient.
7	D	No number can be divided by zero.
| 8 | A | 100 divided by 12<br>is 8 with remainder 4<br>$= 8 \text{ R } 4$<br>$= 8 \frac{4}{12}$<br><br>**Show Work:**<br><br>```
          0 0 8
    1 2 | 1 0 0
          0
          1 0
            0
          1 0 0
            9 6
              4
```<br><br>After filling 8 boxes, there will be a remainder of 4 donuts. |
| 9 | B | Any number divided by 1 remains the same. |
| 10 | B | 680 divided by 40<br>is 17 with remainder 0<br>$= 17 \text{ R } 0$<br>$= 17 \frac{0}{14}$<br><br>**Show Work:**<br><br>```
        0 1 7
  4 0 | 6 8 0
        0
        6 8
        4 0
        2 8 0
        2 8 0
            0
```<br> |

Lesson 7: Multiply Decimals

Question No.	Answer	Detailed Explanations
1	C	To solve, multiply without decimals. Then insert the decimal in your answer. Be sure the product has as many places to the right of the decimal as both factors combined. $\begin{array}{r} \$\ 0.4\ 2 \\ \times\ 8 \\ \hline 1\ 6 \\ +\ 3\ 2\ 0 \\ \hline \$\ 3.3\ 6 \end{array}$
2	0.275	To solve, multiply without decimals. Then insert the decimal in your answer. Be sure the product has as many places to the right of the decimal as both factors. $\begin{array}{r} 0.2\ 5 \\ \times\quad 1.1 \\ \hline 5 \\ 2\ 0 \\ 5\ 0 \\ 2\ 0\ 0 \\ \hline 0.2\ 7\ 5 \end{array}$
3	1.2	To solve, multiply without decimals. Then insert the decimal in your answer. Be sure the product has as many places to the right of the decimal as both factors combined. $\begin{array}{r} 0.3 \\ \times\ 4 \\ \hline 1.2 \end{array}$

Question No.	Answer	Detailed Explanations

4	1.8	To solve, multiply without decimals. Then insert the decimal in your answer. Be sure the product has as many places to the right of the decimal as both factors combined.
		
		   0.6
		 x 3
		———
		  1.8
		————

5	C	To solve, multiply without decimals. Then insert the decimal in your answer. Be sure the product has as many places to the right of the decimal as both factors combined.
		
		   0.1 2
		  x 1 2
		————
		      4
		    2 0
		    2 0
		+ 1 0 0
		————
		  1.4 4

6	C	To solve, multiply without decimals. Then insert the decimal in your answer. Be sure the product has as many places to the right of the decimal as both factors combined.
		
		   2 5
		 x 0.3
		————
		  1 5
		  6 0
		————
		  7.5
		————

Question No.	Answer	Detailed Explanations
7	D	To solve, multiply without decimals. Then insert the decimal in your answer. Be sure the product has as many places to the right of the decimal as both factors combined. $\begin{array}{r} \$\ 0.3\ 5 \\ \times \quad 5 \\ \hline 2\ 5 \\ 1\ 5\ 0 \\ \hline \$\ 1.7\ 5 \end{array}$
8	D	To solve, multiply without decimals. Then insert the decimal in your answer. Be sure the product has as many places to the right of the decimal as both factors combined. $\begin{array}{r} 1.4 \\ \times\ 0.7 \\ \hline 2\ 8 \\ 7\ 0 \\ \hline 0.9\ 8 \end{array}$
9	C	To solve, multiply without decimals. Then insert the decimal in your answer. Be sure the product has as many places to the right of the decimal as both factors combined. $\begin{array}{r} 0.3 \\ \times\ 0.5 \\ \hline 1\ 5 \\ 0\ 0 \\ \hline 0.1\ 5 \end{array}$

Question No.	Answer	Detailed Explanations

10	A	To solve, multiply without decimals. Then insert the decimal in your answer. Be sure the product has as many places to the right of the decimal as both factors combined.
		
		      1.5
		  x 0.5
		  _____
		    2 5
		   5 0
		  _____
		 0.7 5
		  _____

Lesson 8: Divide Decimals

Question No.	Answer	Detailed Explanations
1	0.14	To solve, use division. Divide the numbers without the decimal point. Then, insert a decimal into the answer, leaving the same number of places to the right of the decimal as the dividend. $42 \div 3 = 14 \rightarrow 0.14$
2	0.3	To solve, use division. Move both decimal places to the right one place, so you are dividing by a whole number ($0.9 \div 3$). Divide the numbers without the decimal point. Then, insert a decimal into the answer, leaving the same number of places to the right of the decimal as the dividend (remember that you shifted the decimal to have only one place to the right of the dividend). $9 \div 3 = 3 \rightarrow 0.3$
3	A	To solve, use division. Divide the numbers without the decimal point. Then, insert a decimal into the answer, leaving the same number of places to the right of the decimal as the dividend. $48 \div 2 = 24 \rightarrow 2.4$
4	0.05	To solve, use division. Divide the numbers without the decimal point. Then, insert a decimal into the answer, leaving the same number of places to the right of the decimal as the dividend. $15 \div 3 = 5 \rightarrow 0.05$
5	A	To solve, use division. Divide the numbers without the decimal point. Then, insert a decimal into the answer, leaving the same number of places to the right of the decimal as the dividend. $52 \div 4 = 13 \rightarrow 0.13$
6	D	To solve, use division. Divide the numbers without the decimal point. Then, insert a decimal into the answer, leaving the same number of places to the right of the decimal as the dividend. $36 \div 6 = 6 \rightarrow 0.6$

Question No.	Answer	Detailed Explanations
7	A	To solve, use division. Divide the numbers without the decimal point. Since 6 does not divide evenly by 4, think of it as 0.60. Then, insert a decimal into the answer, leaving the same number of places to the right of the decimal as the dividend (remember, we changed the dividend to use two places to the right of the decimal). $60 \div 4 = 15$ -->0.15
8	C	To solve, use division. Divide the numbers without the decimal point. Since 12 does not divide evenly by 5, think of it as 0.120. Then, insert a decimal into the answer, leaving the same number of places to the right of the decimal as the dividend (remember, we changed the dividend to use three places to the right of the decimal). $120 \div 5 = 24$ -->0.024
9	C	To solve, use division. Divide the numbers without the decimal point. Then, insert a decimal into the answer, leaving the same number of places to the right of the decimal as the dividend. $908 \div 4 = 227$ -->2.27
10	B	To solve, use division. Divide the numbers without the decimal point. Then, insert a decimal into the answer, leaving the same number of places to the right of the decimal as the dividend. $24 \div 6 = 4$ -->0.04

Lesson 9: Add & Subtract Fractions

Question No.	Answer	Detailed Explanations
1	$\frac{3}{10}$	When fractions have a common denominator (in this case 10), just add the numerators (2 + 1 = 3) and keep the denominator the same.
2	A	Add the whole numbers (1+1) to get 2. Then add the fractions. As they have a common denominator of 4, just add the numerators (1+2) to get $\frac{3}{4}$. The total is $2\frac{3}{4}$.
3	$\frac{1}{4}$	As the fractions have a common denominator of 4, just subtract the numerators (3 - 2) to get $\frac{1}{4}$.
4	D	Subtract the whole numbers (3 - 1) to get 2. Then subtract the fractions. Since they have a common denominator of 10, just subtract the numerators (4 - 1) to get $\frac{3}{10}$. The total is $2\frac{3}{10}$.
5	D	Fractions must have a common denominator to be added. Multiply both the numerator and the denominator by 3 to get $\frac{9}{12}$ so that both the fractions have a common denominator 12.
6	C	Fractions must have a common denominator to be added. Multiply both the numerator and the denominator by 2 to get $\frac{2}{4}$. Then add the numerators (2+1) to get the numerator of the sum and keep the common denominator 4, to get the sum, $\frac{3}{4}$.
7	$\frac{5}{9}$	For subtracting fractions (proper or improper), find the common denominator and find the equivalent fractions in terms of this common denominator and subtract them. Then, write the fraction in its simplest form. $\frac{2}{3} = \frac{2 \times 3}{3 \times 3} = \frac{6}{9}$ $\frac{2}{3} - \frac{1}{9} = \frac{6}{9} - \frac{1}{9} = \frac{6-1}{9} = \frac{5}{9}$.
8	D	First add the whole numbers (2 + 5) to get 7. Then add the fraction parts. Since fractions must have a common denominator to be added, find the equivalent fractions in terms of the common denominator and add them. $\frac{1}{2} = \frac{1 \times 4}{2 \times 4} = \frac{4}{8}$. $\frac{1}{8} + \frac{1}{2} = \frac{1}{8} + \frac{4}{8} = \frac{1+4}{8} = \frac{5}{8}$. The total is $7\frac{5}{8}$.

Question No.	Answer	Detailed Explanations
9	A	First add the whole numbers (5 + 1) to get 6. Then add the fraction parts. Since fractions must have a common denominator to be added, find the equivalent fractions in terms of the common denominator and add them. $\frac{1}{4} = \frac{1 \times 2}{4 \times 2} = \frac{2}{8}$ $\frac{5}{8} + \frac{1}{4} = \frac{5}{8} + \frac{2}{8} = \frac{5+2}{8} = \frac{7}{8}$ The total is $6\frac{7}{8}$.
10	D	In order to subtract a fraction from a whole number, convert 1 from the whole number into a fraction with a common denominator. The number 1 can be converted to thirds by changing it to $\frac{3}{3}$. That leaves $4\frac{3}{3} - \frac{1}{3}$. Keep 4 as the whole number & subtract the numerators of the fractions to get $\frac{2}{3}$.

Lesson 10: Problem Solving with Fractions

Question No.	Answer	Detailed Explanations
1	C	Multiply 60 (the number of minutes in an hour) by $\frac{3}{4}$ to find the number of minutes she practiced. $60 \times \frac{3}{4} = \frac{180}{4} = 45$
2	12	Multiply 30 by $\frac{3}{5}$ to find the number of boys. $30 \times \frac{3}{5} = \frac{90}{5} = 18$ If there are 18 boys, there must be 12 girls (30 - 18 = 12).
3	D	To solve, divide 11 miles by 3 hours. Convert the improper fraction to a mixed number. $\frac{11}{3} = 3\frac{2}{3}$
4	D	A whole apple is 1, or $\frac{8}{8}$. To find out how much is not water, subtract the fraction that is water. $\frac{8}{8} - \frac{7}{8} = \frac{1}{8}$
5	5	This problem has a lot of extra information. To find the number of pumpkins that were too small, just multiply the total number of pumpkins (20) by the fraction of pumpkins that were too small ($\frac{1}{4}$). $20 \times \frac{1}{4} = \frac{20}{4} = 5$
6	A	Timothy gave away 9 out of 45 shirts. This can be represented as a fraction by $\frac{9}{45}$ which is equivalent to $\frac{1}{5}$.

Question No.	Answer	Detailed Explanations
7	B	4 out of 32 students come to tutoring. This can be represented as a fraction by $\frac{4}{32}$ which is equivalent to $\frac{1}{8}$.
8	B	She has completed $\frac{14}{35}$ problems. This means she has 21 left to do (35 - 14 = 21). 21 out of 35 is the fraction $\frac{21}{35}$. Since that option is not available, reduce the fraction by dividing both the numerator and denominator by 7. $$\frac{21}{35} = \left(\frac{21}{7}\right) \div \left(\frac{35}{7}\right) = \frac{3}{5}$$
9	20	Multiply 32 by $\frac{2}{8}$ to find the number of points they scored in the second half. $$32 \times \frac{2}{8} = \frac{64}{8} = 8$$ If they scored 8 points in the second half, they must have scored 24 points in the first half (32 - 8 = 24).
10	C	You will only need half the amount of flour, since 24 is half of 48. Multiply 3 cups by $\frac{1}{2}$ to find out how much flour to use. $$3 \times \frac{1}{2} = \frac{3}{2} = 1\frac{1}{2}$$

Lesson 11: Multiply Fractions

Question No.	Answer	Detailed Explanations
1	A	First, multiply the numerators (2 x 4 = 8) then multiply the denominators (3 x 5 = 15) to get the fraction $\frac{8}{15}$.
2	D	Multiply the first two terms first, using $\frac{5}{1}$ for the whole number 5. $\frac{5}{1} \times \frac{2}{3} = \frac{10}{3}$. Then multiply this fraction by the third term: $\frac{10}{3} \times \frac{1}{2} = \frac{10}{6}$ Change the improper fraction $\frac{10}{6}$ to a mixed number by dividing 10 by 6. Then change $1\frac{4}{6}$ into lowest terms, which is $1\frac{2}{3}$.
3	B	Multiplying a fraction by a whole number is the same as multiplying the numerator by a whole number then dividing the product by the denominator.
4	C	The product of two fractions is equal to the product of the numerators divided by the product of the denominators.
5	B	To solve, multiply $\frac{4}{7} \times \frac{3}{5} \times 4$. Multiply the first two terms first: $\frac{4}{7} \times \frac{3}{5} = \frac{12}{35}$ Then multiply this fraction by 4. Remember that the whole number 4 can be shown as the fraction $\frac{4}{1}$. $\frac{12}{35} \times 4 = \frac{48}{35}$ Since $\frac{35}{35}$ is 1 whole the fraction can be shown as the mixed number $1\frac{13}{35}$.
6	C	Multiply 600 by $\frac{1}{3}$ to find the number of seats that are empty. $\frac{600}{1} \times \frac{1}{3} = \frac{600}{3} = 200$
7	C	Three of the options represent 5 whole units and a fractional half. $\frac{25}{50}$ is equivalent to one half and so is 0.500. The improper fraction $\frac{44}{8}$ can be changed to a mixed number by dividing 44 by 8 to get $5\frac{4}{8}$ (which is equal to $5\frac{1}{2}$). The fraction $5\frac{1}{5}$ is not equivalent to the other three.

Question No.	Answer	Detailed Explanations
8	$\dfrac{1}{8}$	Multiply the numerators ($1 \times 1 = 1$) then multiply the denominators ($2 \times 4 = 8$) to get the fraction $\dfrac{1}{8}$.
9	$\dfrac{3}{8}$	To solve, multiply $\dfrac{1}{2} \times \dfrac{3}{4}$. First, multiply the numerators ($1 \times 3 = 3$) then multiply the denominators ($2 \times 4 = 8$) to get the fraction $\dfrac{3}{8}$.
10	$\dfrac{1}{20}$	To solve, multiply $\dfrac{1}{2} \times \dfrac{1}{10}$. First, multiply the numerators ($1 \times 1 = 1$) then multiply the denominators ($2 \times 10 = 20$) to get the fraction $\dfrac{1}{20}$.

Lesson 12: Real World Problems with Fractions

Question No.	Answer	Detailed Explanations
1	A	To multiply a whole number by a fraction, represent the whole number as $\frac{17}{1}$. Then, multiply numerators (17 x 3 = 51) to find the numerator and multiply denominators (1 x 4 = 4) to find the denominator. Change the improper fraction $\frac{51}{4}$ to a mixed number by dividing 51 by 4 to equal $12\frac{3}{4}$.
2	A	To find how far the teammates ran, subtract $\frac{3}{5}$ (Carl's distance) from $\frac{5}{5}$ (the total distance) to get $\frac{2}{5}$. Then, multiply this fraction by the distance of the race. Multiply numerators (2 x 9 = 18) to find the numerator and multiply denominators (5 x 10 = 50) to find the denominator. Reduce the fraction $\frac{18}{50}$ to $\frac{9}{25}$.
3	B	To multiply a whole number by a mixed number, first change the whole number to a fraction ($\frac{3}{1}$) and change the mixed number to a fraction ($\frac{9}{5}$). Multiply numerators (3 x 9 = 27) to find the numerator and multiply denominators (1 x 5 = 5) to find the denominator. The improper fraction $\frac{27}{5}$ can be changed to the mixed number $5\frac{2}{5}$
4	C	To multiply a fraction by a mixed number, change the mixed number to a fraction ($\frac{16}{5}$). Multiply numerators (2 x 16 = 32) to find the numerator and multiply denominators (3 x 5 = 15) to find the denominator. The improper fraction $\frac{32}{15}$ can be changed to the mixed number $2\frac{2}{15}$.
5	B	To multiply a mixed number by a mixed number, change each mixed number to a fraction ($\frac{41}{2}$ and $\frac{9}{2}$). Multiply numerators (41 x 9 = 369) to find the numerator and multiply denominators (2 x 2 = 4) to find the denominator. The improper fraction $\frac{369}{4}$ can be changed to the mixed number $92\frac{1}{4}$.

Question No.	Answer	Detailed Explanations
6	A	To multiply a whole number by a mixed number, first change the whole number to a fraction ($\frac{20}{1}$) and change the mixed number to a fraction ($\frac{14}{3}$). Multiply numerators (20 x 14 = 280) to find the numerator and multiply denominators (1 x 3 = 3) to find the denominator. The improper fraction $\frac{280}{3}$ can be changed to the mixed number $93\frac{1}{3}$.
7	D	To multiply a whole number by a mixed number, first change the whole number to a fraction ($\frac{6}{1}$) and change the mixed number to a fraction ($\frac{9}{8}$). Multiply numerators (9 x 6 = 54) to find the numerator and multiply denominators (1 x 8 = 8) to find the denominator. The improper fraction $\frac{54}{8}$ can be changed to the mixed number $6\frac{6}{8}$.
8	$26\frac{1}{4}$	To multiply a whole number by a mixed number, first change the whole number to a fraction ($\frac{21}{1}$) and change the mixed number to a fraction ($\frac{5}{4}$). Multiply numerators (21 x 5 = 105) to find the numerator and multiply denominators (1 x 4 = 4) to find the denominator. The improper fraction $\frac{105}{4}$ can be changed to the mixed number $26\frac{1}{4}$.
9	$4\frac{2}{3}$	To change $\frac{14}{3}$ to a mixed number, divide 14 by 3. The number 4 remainder 2 is written as $4\frac{2}{3}$ because the remaining 2 still needs to be divided by 3.
10	21	Each whole foot has $\frac{4}{4}$ and Danny needs 5 whole feet, so 5 x $\frac{4}{4}$ = $\frac{20}{4}$. He also needs $\frac{1}{4}$ more, so that's $\frac{21}{4}$ total. He will need 21 pieces that are $\frac{1}{4}$ foot long.

Lesson 13: Dividing by unit fractions

Question No.	Answer	Detailed Explanations
1	6	The first step in dividing by a fraction is to find its reciprocal, which is the reverse of its numerator and denominator. The fraction $\frac{1}{3}$ becomes $\frac{3}{1}$, or the whole number 3. Then solve by multiplying. $2\times3=6$.
2	A	The first step in dividing by a fraction is to find its reciprocal, which is the reverse of its numerator and denominator.
3	$4\frac{1}{2}$	The first step in dividing by a fraction is to find its reciprocal, which is the reverse of its numerator and denominator. The fraction $\frac{2}{3}$ becomes $\frac{3}{2}$. Then solve by multiplying (use $\frac{3}{1}$ for the whole number 3): $\frac{3}{1}\times\frac{3}{2}=\frac{9}{2}=4\frac{1}{2}$.
4	C	Dividing by a number less than one causes the original number to become larger. When dividing by a fraction less than 1, multiplying by its reciprocal will create a situation in which you multiply by a larger number and divide by a smaller number, therefore increasing the size.
5	D	To divide $\frac{1}{3}$ by 5, multiply $\frac{1}{3}$ by the reciprocal of 5, which is $\frac{1}{5}$. $\frac{1}{3}\times\frac{1}{5}=\frac{1}{15}$.
6	B	To divide $\frac{1}{8}$ by 4, multiply $\frac{1}{8}$ by the reciprocal of 4, which is $\frac{1}{4}$. $\frac{1}{8}\times\frac{1}{4}=\frac{1}{32}$
7	30	To solve, divide 10 by $\frac{1}{3}$, multiply 10 (or $\frac{10}{1}$) by the reciprocal of $\frac{1}{3}$, which is $\frac{3}{1}$. $\frac{10}{1}\times\frac{3}{1}=\frac{30}{1}$
8	D	When dividing two numbers (such as $12\div4=3$), the answer can be checked by multiplying ($3\times4=12$). This is true for fractions as well. To check $\frac{1}{6}\div3=\frac{1}{18}$, multiply: $\frac{1}{18}\times\frac{3}{1}=\frac{3}{18}=\frac{1}{6}$
9	C	To solve, divide 8 by $\frac{1}{4}$, multiply 8(or $\frac{8}{1}$) by the reciprocal of $\frac{1}{4}$, which is $\frac{4}{1}$. $\frac{8}{1}\times\frac{4}{1}=\frac{32}{1}=32$

Question No.	Answer	Detailed Explanations
10	C	When dividing two numbers (such as $12 \div 4 = 3$), the answer can be checked by multiplying ($3 \times 4 = 12$). This is true for fractions as well. To check $10 \div \frac{1}{4} = 40$, multiply: $40 \times \frac{1}{4} = 10$

Lesson 14: Rational Numbers, Addition & Subtraction

Question No.	Answer	Detailed Explanation
1	16.775	Remember: adding and subtracting rational numbers works just like integers. If you need to carry or borrow, the rules remain the same. 25 + 2.005 - 7.253 - 2.977 27.005 - 7.253 - 2.977 , 19.752 - 2.977 = 16.775
2	A	$-3\frac{4}{5} + 9\frac{7}{10} - 2\frac{11}{20} = -3\frac{16}{20} + 9\frac{14}{20} - 2\frac{11}{20}$ $-5\frac{27}{20} + 9\frac{14}{20} = -5\frac{27}{20} + 8\frac{34}{20}$, $3\frac{7}{20}$ is the correct answer.
3	C	They spent 6 hours and 5 min total on their trip. Of that time, 4 hours and 50 minutes were spent driving. $4\frac{5}{6}$ hrs driving out of 6 $\frac{1}{12}$ hours. Converting into improper fractions we get $(\frac{29}{6})$ out of $(\frac{73}{12})$. $(\frac{29}{6}) \times (\frac{12}{73}) = \frac{58}{73}$ hours spent driving
4	B	If $a = \frac{5}{6}$, $b = -\frac{2}{3}$ and $c = -1\frac{1}{3}$, find a - b - c. $\frac{5}{6} - (-\frac{2}{3}) - (-1\frac{1}{3})$ $= \frac{5}{6} + \frac{4}{6} + 1\frac{2}{6} = 1\frac{11}{6} = 2\frac{5}{6}$. $2\frac{5}{6}$ is the correct answer.
5	B	Starting with a full candy bar, we take away $\frac{1}{2}$ leaving $\frac{1}{2}$. Then we take away $\frac{1}{2}$ of the remaining half leaving $\frac{1}{4}$ of the original candy bar. Then we take away half of the $\frac{1}{4}$ leaving $\frac{1}{8}$ of the original bar. $\frac{1}{8}$ is the correct answer.
6	A and C	$-\frac{6}{4} + \frac{3}{4}$ add the numerators and you get -3. So the fraction is $-\frac{3}{4}$ $\frac{1}{8} - \frac{7}{8} = 1 - 7 = -6$ and $\frac{-6}{8}$ simplifies to $\frac{-3}{4}$

Question No.	Answer	Detailed Explanation
7	D	On his second trip to the store he paid $74.99 plus half of $68.55. $74.99 + $34.28 = $109.27 $159.95 - 109.27 = $50.68 $50.68 is the correct answer.
8	B	First, we will change 5 1/2 to 5.5. Then we have 3.24 - 1.914 - 6.025 +9.86 -2.2 + 5.5 = 8.461 8.461 is the correct answer.
9	C	To solve this problem, list all the monetary values, along with the proper operation, before evaluating it. For this problem, words like "give" mean to subtract, while "receives" means to add. (1) 76.00 - 42.45 - 21.34 + 14.50 = (2) 33.55 - 21.34 + 14.50 = (3) 12.21 + 14.50 = (4) 26.71 Therefore, John will have $26.71 later that night.
10	$660	Year 1 - $12.00, Year 2 - $24.00. Year 3 - $36.00. Year 4 - $48.00. Year 5 - $60.00. Year 6 - $72.00. Year 7 - $84.00. Year 8 - $96.00. Year 9 - $108.00. Year 10 - $120.00 Adding the totals for each year, we get $660.00. $660.00 is the correct answer.

Lesson 15: Divide whole numbers by unit fractions and unit fractions by whole numbers.

Question No.	Answer	Detailed Explanations
1	B	Division can be checked by multiplying the quotient by the divisor to equal the dividend. In this case, $24 \times \frac{1}{4} = \frac{24}{4} = 6$.
2	D	In option D, each of four units is divided into thirds, resulting in a total of 12 units. Option B also produces 12 units, but it shows 3 units divided into fourths.
3	D	The model shows each of three units divided into eighths, resulting in a total of 24 units. That is shown as $3 \div \frac{1}{8} = 24$. Although option C is a true statement, it does not represent the model.
4	A	To solve, divide the 5 pieces of wood into fifths: $5 \div \frac{1}{5} = 5 \times 5 = 25$
5	C	To solve, divide the 10 yards of fabric into thirds: $10 \div \frac{1}{3} = 10 \times 3 = 30$
6	B	When dividing a whole number by a fraction, rewrite the whole number as a fraction with a denominator of 1. Then multiply by the multiplicative inverse of the fraction. Finally, simplify the answer. $4 \div \frac{1}{5} = \frac{4}{1} \times \frac{5}{1} = \frac{20}{1} = 20$. B is the right answer choice.

Question No.	Answer	Detailed Explanations
7		

Statements	True	False
$\frac{1}{12} \div 4 > 40$		✓
$\frac{1}{4} \div 7 = \frac{1}{14}$		✓
$\frac{1}{3} \div 33 < 5$	✓	
$\frac{1}{8} \div 4 < \frac{1}{2}$	✓	

1) $\frac{1}{12} \div \frac{4}{1} = \frac{1}{12} \times \frac{1}{4} = \frac{1}{48}$; Therefore $\frac{1}{48} < 40$.

2) $\frac{1}{4} \div 7 = \frac{1}{4} \div \frac{7}{1} = \frac{1}{4} \times \frac{1}{7} = \frac{1}{28}$; Therefore $\frac{1}{28} \neq \frac{1}{14}$

3) $\frac{1}{3} \div 33 = \frac{1}{3} \div \frac{33}{1} = \frac{1}{3} \times \frac{1}{33} = \frac{1}{99}$; Therefore $\frac{1}{99} < 5$

4) $\frac{1}{8} \div 4 = \frac{1}{8} \div \frac{4}{1} = \frac{1}{8} \times \frac{1}{4} = \frac{1}{32}$; Therefore $\frac{1}{32} < \frac{1}{2}$

Question No. 8

When trying to find a divisor when working with fractions quotients, rewrite the question as a multiplication question.

A. $\frac{1}{8} \times \frac{1}{14} = \frac{1}{112} \rightarrow \frac{1}{8} \div 14 = \frac{1}{112}$

B. $\frac{1}{3} \times \frac{1}{29} = \frac{1}{87} \rightarrow \frac{1}{3} \div 29 = \frac{1}{87}$

C. $\frac{1}{9} \times \frac{1}{55} = \frac{1}{495} \rightarrow \frac{1}{9} \div 55 = \frac{1}{495}$

Question No. 9 — Answer: A

$8 \div \frac{1}{3} = 8 \times 3 = 24$. The answer choice A is the correct answer.

Question No. 10 — Answer: B

$4 \div \frac{7}{21} = 4 \times \frac{21}{7}$

$= 4 \times 3$
$= 12$
B is the correct answer choice.

Chapter 2
Computations and Algebraic Relationships

Chapter 2

Lesson 1: Identify prime and composite numbers

1. Andrew has a chart containing the numbers 1 through 100. He is going to put an "X" on all of the multiples of 10 and a circle around all of the multiples of 4. How many numbers will have an "X", but will not be circled?

Ⓐ 3
Ⓑ 4
Ⓒ 5
Ⓓ 8

2. Which number are multiple of 30?

Ⓐ 3
Ⓑ 6
Ⓒ 60
Ⓓ 270

3. Use the Venn diagram below to respond to the following question.

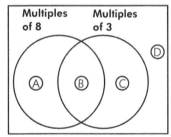

In which region of the diagram would the number 72 be found?

Ⓐ Region A
Ⓑ Region B
Ⓒ Region C
Ⓓ Region D

4. Which numbers can divide 28 evenly?

Ⓐ 3
Ⓑ 4
Ⓒ 7
Ⓓ 5

5. Use the Venn diagram below to respond to the following question. Which of the following numbers would be found in Region D?

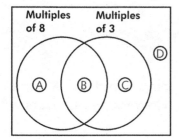

    Ⓐ   41
    Ⓑ   53
    Ⓒ   62
    Ⓓ   All of the above

6. Which of these sets contains no composite numbers?

    Ⓐ   97, 71, 59, 29
    Ⓑ   256, 155, 75, 15
    Ⓒ   5, 23, 87, 91
    Ⓓ   2, 11, 19, 51

7. Choose the set that consists of only prime numbers.

    Ⓐ   2, 4, 8, 12
    Ⓑ   13, 15, 17, 19
    Ⓒ   2, 5, 23, 29
    Ⓓ   3, 17, 29, 81

8. Which of the following sets include factors of 44?

    Ⓐ   2, 4, 11, 22
    Ⓑ   0, 2, 6, 11
    Ⓒ   2, 4, 12, 22
    Ⓓ   4, 8, 12, 22

9. Which number completes the following number sentences?

$$72 \div \underline{\hspace{1cm}} = 6$$
$$\underline{\hspace{1cm}} \times 6 = 72$$

10. If Carla wants to complete exactly 63 push ups during her workout, it is best if she does her push-ups in sets of _____.

   Ⓐ   13
   Ⓑ   8
   Ⓒ   7
   Ⓓ   17

Lesson 2: Solve multi-step problems involving the four operations

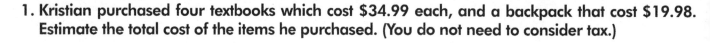

1. Kristian purchased four textbooks which cost $34.99 each, and a backpack that cost $19.98. Estimate the total cost of the items he purchased. (You do not need to consider tax.)

   Ⓐ $90.00
   Ⓑ $160.00
   Ⓒ $120.00
   Ⓓ $55.00

2. During the last three games of the season, the attendance at the Tigers' home games was 14,667; 16,992; and 18,124. Estimate the total attendance for these three games. Round to the nearest thousand.

   Ⓐ 60,000
   Ⓑ 45,000
   Ⓒ 50,000
   Ⓓ 47,000

3. Steven keeps his baseball cards in an album. He has filled 147 pages of the album. He can fit 9 cards on each page. Which of the following statements is true?

   Ⓐ Steven has more than 2,000 baseball cards.
   Ⓑ Steven has between 1,000 and 1,500 baseball cards.
   Ⓒ Steven has between 1,500 and 2,000 baseball cards.
   Ⓓ Steven has less than 1,000 baseball cards.

4. Jam jars can be packed in large boxes of 60 or small boxes of 25. There are 700 jam jars to be shipped. The supplier wants to use the least number of boxes possible, but the boxes cannot be only partially filled. How many large boxes will the supplier end up using?

   Ⓐ 10 large boxes
   Ⓑ 11 large boxes
   Ⓒ 12 large boxes
   Ⓓ   It is not possible to ship all 700 jars.

5. Allison needs 400 feet of rope to put a border around her yard. She can buy the rope in lengths of 36 feet. How many 36 foot long ropes will she need to buy?

Ⓐ   9 ropes
Ⓑ   10 ropes
Ⓒ   11 ropes
Ⓓ   12 ropes.

6. When the expression 3(n + 7) is evaluated for a given value of n, the result is 33. What is the value of n?

7. Which number is acting as a coefficient in this expression? 360 + 22x − 448

8. Evaluate the following when n = 7: 5(n − 5)

9. For which of the following values of b does the expression 4b − 9 have a value between 90 and 100?

Ⓐ   b = 104
Ⓑ   b = 26
Ⓒ   b = 48
Ⓓ   b = 24

10. Evaluate the following when n = −4: [5n − 3n] + 2n

Ⓐ   b = 16
Ⓑ   b = −20
Ⓒ   b = −16
Ⓓ   b = 0

Chapter 2

Lesson 3: Analyze Patterns and Relationships

1. **Which set of numbers completes the function table?**
   Rule: multiply by 3

Input	Output
1	☐
2	☐
5	15
8	☐
12	☐

   Ⓐ 4, 5, 11, 15
   Ⓑ 3, 6, 24, 36
   Ⓒ 3, 6, 32, 48
   Ⓓ 11, 12, 18, 112

2. **Which set of numbers completes the function table?**
   Rule: add 4, then divide by 2

Input	Output
4	☐
6	☐
10	7
22	☐
40	☐

   Ⓐ 1, 3, 19, 37
   Ⓑ 10, 12, 28, 46
   Ⓒ 4, 5, 13, 22
   Ⓓ 16, 20, 52, 88

3. Which set of coordinate pairs matches the function table?
   Rule: multiply by 2, then subtract 1

Input	Output
5	☐
9	17
14	☐
25	☐

Ⓐ (5 , 9), (9 , 17), (14 , 27), (25 , 49)
Ⓑ (5 , 9), (14 , 25), (9 , 17), (27 , 49)
Ⓒ (5 , 9), (9 , 17), (17 , 14), (14 , 25)
Ⓓ (5 , 11), (9 , 17), (14 , 29), (25 , 51)

4. Which set of coordinate pairs matches the function table?
   Rule: divide by 3, then add 2

Input	Output
9	☐
15	7
27	☐
33	☐

Ⓐ (9 , 1), (15 , 7), (27 , 19), (33 , 25)
Ⓑ (9 , 5), (15 , 7), (27 , 11), (33 , 13)
Ⓒ (9 , 11), (15 , 7), (27 , 29), (33 , 35)
Ⓓ (9 , 15), (15 , 7), (7 , 27), (27 , 33)

5. Which set of numbers completes the function table?
Rule: subtract 4

Input	Output
☐	1
7	3
☐	7
☐	10
☐	15

Ⓐ 0, 3, 6, 11
Ⓑ 3, 10, 17, 25
Ⓒ 4, 28, 40, 60
Ⓓ 5, 11, 14, 19

6. Which set of numbers completes the function table?
Rule: add 1, then multiply by 5

Input	Output
☐	5
2	15
☐	20
☐	35
☐	55

Ⓐ 2, 5, 15, 20
Ⓑ 1, 4, 7, 11
Ⓒ 30, 105, 180, 280
Ⓓ 0, 3, 6, 10

7. Which rule describes the function table?

x	y
11	5
14	8
21	15
28	22

Ⓐ Add 3
Ⓑ Subtract 6
Ⓒ Subtract 1, then divide by 2
Ⓓ Divide by 2, Add 1

8. Which rule describes the function table?

x	y
4	4
7	10
13	22
20	36

Ⓐ Multiply by 2, then subtract 4
Ⓑ Add zero
Ⓒ Add 3
Ⓓ Subtract 1, then multiply by 2

9. Which describes the graph of this function plotted on a coordinate grid?

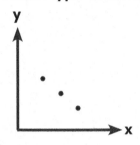

x	y
11	5
14	8
21	15
28	22

Ⓐ A curving line
Ⓑ A horizontal line
Ⓒ An upward sloping line
Ⓓ A downward sloping line

10. Which type of function would result in a graph that looks like this?

Ⓐ One in which x and y increase at fixed rates
Ⓑ One in which x and y decrease at fixed rates
Ⓒ One in which x decreases while y remains constant.
Ⓓ One in which x increases while y decreases

Chapter 2

Lesson 4: Write and Interpret Numerical Expressions & Patterns

1. Which of the following number sentences models the Associative Property of Multiplication? Circle the correct answer choice.

Ⓐ $80 \times 5 = (40 \times 5) + (40 \times 5)$
Ⓑ $(11 \times 6) \times 7 = 11 \times (6 \times 7)$
Ⓒ $2 \times 3 \times 4 = 4 \times 3 \times 1 + 1$
Ⓓ $44 \times 1 = 44$

2. What is the value of $2 \times [5-(6 \div 3)]$?

3. Identify the expression that equals 2?

Ⓐ $[(3 \times 2) + 4] \div 5$
Ⓑ $2 \times [(5 \times 4) \div 10]$
Ⓒ $12 - [(4 + 8) \div 3]$

4. Evaluate the expression $(8 \times 6) + (8-3)$?

Ⓐ 53
Ⓑ 48
Ⓒ 64
Ⓓ 81

5. Where must the parentheses be in the following expression so that the answer is 6?
   $20 - 8 \div 2$

Ⓐ $20 - (8 \div 2)$
Ⓑ $(20 - 8) \div 2$

6. Evaluate the expression 4 x (2 + 1) + 6.

   Ⓐ 18
   Ⓑ 15
   Ⓒ 21
   Ⓓ 16

7. In a drawing class, crayons were distributed to 12 students. Six of the students got packets that had 8 crayons and the other six got packets that had 10 crayons. How many crayons were distributed in all?

   Ⓐ 110
   Ⓑ 108
   Ⓒ 100
   Ⓓ 112

8. Jeremy had 20 books which he arranged on 4 shelves of a rack. His brother, Barndon takes away 4 books from each of the shelves. How many books are there now in each shelf?

   Ⓐ 4
   Ⓑ 5
   Ⓒ 8
   Ⓓ 1

9. Mary has 15 chocolates that she wants to put into packs of 3. She wants to give these packs to 4 of her friends. Choose the expression that fits the story.

   Ⓐ (15 ÷ 3) + 4
   Ⓑ (15 × 3) + 4
   Ⓒ (15 × 3) − 4
   Ⓓ (15 ÷ 3) − 4

10. Rewrite the equation below substituting a number value for 'a' and an operation for the question mark that would result in a solution of 10.
    20 ÷ [5 - (a ? 9)] = 10

End of Computations and Algebraic Relationships

Answer Key and
Detailed Explanations

Chapter 2:
Computations and Algebraic Relationships

Lesson 1: Identify prime and composite numbers

Question No.	Answer	Detailed Explanation
1	C	Multiples are the products of two numbers. Skip count, recite timetables or refer to a chart to find all of the multiples of both numbers, from 1 to 100. Listing these multiples may also be helpful: Multiples of 10 are 10, 20, 30, 40, 50, 60, 70, etc. and that of 4 are 4, 8, 12, 16, 20, 24, 28, 32, etc. All of the multiples of 10 will have an x and all of multiples of 4 will be circled. The question to the problem is **how many numbers will have an x, but** *not* **be circled.** In the list of 10 multiples, circle all the multiples of 4. Count the number of multiples of 10 that do not have a circle.
2	C and D	The multiple of 30 must be a product of 30 x another number. 60 = 30 x 2. 270 = 30 x 9
3	B	In this diagram, Section A would contain the multiples of 8 which are not multiples of 3. Section C would contain the multiples of 3 which are not multiples of 8. Section B would contain multiples of both 8 and 3. Section D would list numbers that are **not** multiples of 8 or 3. 8 x 9 = 72 and 3 x 24 = 72, so 72 would be found in Section B.
4	B and C	Use the inverse relationship between multiplication and division to choose the number that is a factor of 28. 28 is a multiple of 7, so 7 is a factor of 28. Similarly, 28 is a multiple of 4, so 4 is a factor of 28
5	D	Refer to the lists of the multiples of 8 and 3. The D section of the Venn diagram is for numbers that are not multiples of 8 or 3. 41, 53, and 62 are not multiples of 3 or 8.
6	A	Any whole number greater than 1 is either classified as composite or prime. A prime number is a number that has only 2 factors - itself and 1. The first set of numbers fits this criteria. All four of the numbers in the set have only two factors.
7	C	Prime numbers are numbers greater than 1 that have only two factors: themselves and the number 1.
8	A	Choose the set that gives the product of 44 when multiplied with another number in that set.
9	12	12 x 6 = 72, so 72 ÷ 12 = 6
10	C	63 is a multiple of 7. 63 is not a multiple of 13, 8, or 17. In order to do exactly 63 push-ups, Carla is best to do sets of 7.

Lesson 2: Solve multi-step problems involving the four operations

Question No.	Answer	Detailed Explanation
1	B	Round off the cost of the textbooks to the nearest dollar. $34.99 is close to $35.00. Round off the price of the backpack from $19.98 to $20.00. The estimated amount Kristian paid can be found by calculating 4 x $35.00 + $20.00. 4 x $35.00 = $140.00; $140.00 + 20.00= $160.00
2	C	To find the estimated total, round each number to the nearest thousand, then add. 14,667 rounds to 15,000; 16,992 rounds to 17,000; and 18,124 rounds to 18,000. 15,000 + 17,000 + 18,000 = 50,000
3	B	To decide which choice is true, use estimation. Steven has filled about 150 pages in his album. (147 is close to 150.) There are about 10 cards on each page. Therefore, he has about 1,500 cards. (150 x 10 = 1,500) Since both of the numbers were rounded up, this estimate is an overestimate. Steven, therefore, has slightly less than 1,500 cards. The second choice is the most reasonable.
4	A	The best option for the supplier would be to use as many large boxes as possible. The supplier would be able to ship 600 jars in 10 large boxes and 100 jars in 4 small boxes. The supplier could not use any more large boxes, because 11 large boxes would contain 660 jars. That would leave 40 more jars to be shipped. That cannot be done without sending a partially-filled box.
5	D	If Allison were to buy 10 ropes, she would have 360 feet of rope. (36 x 10 = 360) Buying one more rope would bring her total up to 396 feet. (360 + 36 = 396) She is still 4 feet short. Therefore, Allison will have to buy 12 ropes in order to get at least 400 feet of rope.
6	4	Since $3(n + 7)$ is equal to 33, then $(n + 7)$ must equal 11 (3 x 11 = 33). Therefore, n must equal 4, since 4 + 7 = 11.
7	22	A number joined to a variable through multiplication is a coefficient. 22 is the coefficient of x.
8	10	When n = 7, the expression becomes $5(7 - 5) = 5 (2) = 10$.
9	B	When b = 26, $4b - 9 = 4(26) - 9 = 104 - 9 = 95$

Question No.	Answer	Detailed Explanation
10	C	When n = −4, the expression becomes: = [5(-4) − 3(-4)] + 2(-4) = [−20 − (−12)] − 8 = [−20 + 12] − 8 = [−8] − 8 = −16 Alternative Solution: [5n-3n]+2n = 2n + 2n = 4n = 4*(-4) = -16

Lesson 3: Analyze Patterns and Relationships

Question No.	Answer	Detailed Explanations
1	B	The rule is to multiply by 3, so plugging in each input number results in the following: 1 x 3 = 3, 2 x 3 = 6, 8 x 3 = 24, 12 x 3 = 36.
2	C	The rule is add 4, then divide by 2, so plugging in each input number results in the following: $(4 + 4) \div 2 = 4, (6 + 4) \div 2 = 5, (22 + 4) \div 2 = 13, (40 + 4) \div 2 = 22$.
3	A	The rule is multiply by 2, then subtract 1, so plugging in each input number results in the following: 5 x 2 - 1 = 9, 9 x 2 - 1 = 17, 14 x 2 - 1 = 27, 25 x 2 - 1 = 49. To create coordinate pairs, write the input number followed by the output number, separated by a comma, in parentheses.
4	B	The rule is divide by 3, then add 2, so plugging in each input number results in the following: $9 \div 3 + 2 = 5, 15 \div 3 + 2 = 7, 27 \div 3 + 2 = 11, 33 \div 3 + 2 = 13$. To create coordinate pairs, write the input number followed by the output number, separated by a comma, in parentheses.
5	D	The rule is -4, Option (A) is incorrect. because 0 -4 = -4 and not 1. (If the rule does not work for one number, we need not check for other numbers). Option (B) is incorrect, because 3 - 4 = -1 and not 1. Option (C) is incorrect, because 4 - 4 = 0 and not 1. All the numbers in option (D) satisfy the rule. 5 – 4 = 1, 11 – 4 = 7, 14 – 4 = 10, 19 – 4 = 15
6	D	The rule is +1, x5, Option (A) is incorrect, because (2 + 1) x 5 = 15 not 5. (If the rule does not work for one number, we need not check for other numbers). Option (B) is incorrect, because (1 + 1) x 5 =10 not 5 Option (C) is incorrect, because (30 + 1) x 5 = 155 not 5 All the numbers in option (D) satisfy the rule. $(0 + 1) \times 5 = 5, (3 + 1) \times 5 = 20, (6 + 1) \times 5 = 35, (10 + 1) \times 5 = 55$.
7	B	Option (A) is incorrect, because 11 + 3 = 14 NOT 5. Option (B) is correct, as subtracting 6 from each x-value results in the corresponding y-value as follows: 11 – 6 = 5, 14 – 6 = 8, 21 – 6 = 15, 28 – 6 = 22. Note that, once we get the correct option, we need not check other options.

Question No.	Answer	Detailed Explanations
8	A	Option (A) is correct because multiplying each x-value by 2 and then subtracting 4 results in the corresponding y-value as follows: 4 x 2 – 4 = 4, 7 x 2 – 4 = 10,13 x 2 – 4 = 22, 20 x 2 – 4 = 36. Note that, once we get the correct option, we need not check other options.
9	C	As the value of x increases, the value of y increases, both at fixed rates. This produces an upward-sloping straight line.
10	D	If the value of x increases while the value of y decreases, the function produces a downward sloping straight line.

Lesson 4: Write and Interpret Numerical Expressions and Patterns

Question No.	Answer	Detailed Explanations
1	B	The Associative Property of Multiplication states that when three or more numbers are multiplied, the product will be the same no matter how the three numbers are grouped. In this example, multiplying 11 x 6 x 7 will produce the same result whether the 11 x 6 are grouped together in parentheses or the 6 x 7 are grouped together. The other options are all mathematically correct, but they show different properties of multiplication.
2	6	When working with parentheses ( ) and brackets [ ], work from the inside to the outside. First solve the expression in the parentheses. 2 x [5 - (6 ÷ 3)] = 2 x [5 - (2)] Next solve the expression in the brackets. 2 x [5 - (2)] = 2 x [3] Finally, solve the resulting expression. 2 x [3] = 6
3	A	When working with parentheses ( ) and brackets [ ], work from the inside to the outside. [(3 x 2) + 4] ÷ 5 = [6 + 4] ÷ 5 = 10 ÷ 5 = 2 2 x [(5 x 4) ÷ 10] = 2 x [20 ÷ 10] = 2 x 2 = 4 12 - [(4 + 8) ÷ 3] = 12 - [12 ÷ 3] = 12 - 4 = 8
4	A	First, evaluate the numbers within brackets 8 x 6 = 48 8 - 3 = 5 Now, in step 2, add both the numbers. 48 + 5 = 53. Hence, A is the correct answer choice.
5	B	Choice A will be 20 - 4 = 16, while choice B is 12 ÷ 2 = 6. Hence, B is the correct answer choice.
6	A	4 x (2 + 1) + 6 = 4 x 3 + 6 = 12 + 6 = 18 Hence, answer choice A is correct.

Question No.	Answer	Detailed Explanations
7	B	$6 \times 8 = 48$ $6 \times 10 = 60$ $48 + 60 = 108$. Hence, answer choice B is correct.
8	D	The problem can be written as $(20 \div 4) - (1 \times 4)$ On solving, we get, $5 - 4 = 1$ Hence, answer choice D is the correct answer choice.
9	D	15 chocolates put into packs of 3 can be written as $(15 \div 3)$. She gives it to 4 of her friends. Hence, $(15 \div 3) - 4$ is the correct answer. Hence, D is the correct answer choice.
10		Think twenty divided by what is ten. Twenty divided by 2 is 10. Therefore two must equal what is in the brackets, $2=[5-(a \, ? \, 9)]$. Next think, five minus what is two. Five minus three is two. Therefore three must equal what is in the parentheses, $3=(a \, ? \, 9)$. Now, we can get 3 by subtracting 9 from 12. $3=12-9$ We can also divide 27 by 9 to get 3. $3 = 27 \div 9$ Can you think of other ways?

Chapter 3:
Geometry and Measurement

Chapter 3

Lesson 1: Real World Problems with Volume

1. Michael packed a box full of 1 ft cubes. The box held 54 cubes. Which of these could be the box Michael packed?

Ⓐ
2 ft
3 ft
6 ft

Ⓑ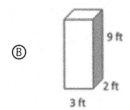
9 ft
2 ft
3 ft

Ⓒ
4 ft
4 ft
4 ft

Ⓓ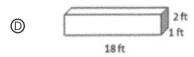
2 ft
1 ft
18 ft

2. A container is shaped like a rectangular prism. The area of its base is 30 in². If the container is 5 inches tall, how many 1 inch cubes can it hold?

3. A rectangular prism has a volume of 300 cm³. If the area of its base is 25 cm² how tall is the prism?

4. Antonia wants to buy a jewelry box with the greatest volume. She measures the length, width, and height of four different jewelry boxes. Which one should she buy to have the greatest volume?

Ⓐ 10 in x 7 in x 4 in
Ⓑ 8 in x 5 in x 5 in
Ⓒ 12 in x 5 in x 5 in
Ⓓ 14 in x 2 in x 10 in

5. Damien is building a file cabinet that must hold 20 ft³. He has created a base for the cabinet that is 4 ft by 1 ft. How tall should he build the cabinet?

6. Bethany has a small rectangular garden that is 32 inches long by 14 inches wide. The average depth of the soil is 2 inches. If Bethany wanted to replace the soil, how much would she need? Circle the correct answer choice.

Ⓐ 448 in³
Ⓑ 896 in³
Ⓒ 450 in³
Ⓓ 48 in³

7. A building has a volume of 1520 ft³. The area of the base of the building is 95 ft².
What is the height of the building?

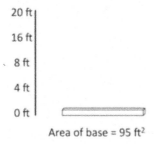

Area of base = 95 ft²

Ⓐ 20ft
Ⓑ 16ft
Ⓒ 8ft
Ⓓ 4ft

8. Melanie has a jewelry box with the volume of 36 cubic cms. If the width is 4 cms and the height is 3 cms, then what is the length of the box?

Ⓐ 4 cms
Ⓑ 3 cms
Ⓒ 5 cms
Ⓓ 12 cms

9. Henry is building an aquarium. The length of the aquarium is 4 feet, width is 3 feet and the height is 5 feet. What will be the volume of the aquarium?

Ⓐ 64 cubic feet
Ⓑ 72 cubic feet
Ⓒ 60 cubic feet
Ⓓ 81 cubic feet.

10. Volume of a clothes box is 2m x 1m x 2m. 15 such boxes must be loaded in a tanker. What will be the total volume occupied by the boxes?

Ⓐ 72 cubic meters
Ⓑ 64 cubic meters
Ⓒ 81 cubic meters
Ⓓ 60 cubic meters

Chapter 3

Lesson 2: Perimeter & Area

1. **A rectangular room measures 10 feet long and 13 feet wide. How could you find out the area of this room?**

    Ⓐ Add 10 and 13, then double the results
    Ⓑ Multiply 10 by 13
    Ⓒ Add 10 and 13
    Ⓓ None of the above

2. **A rectangle has a perimeter of 30 inches. Which of the following could be the dimensions of the rectangle?**

    Ⓐ 10 inches long and 5 inches wide
    Ⓑ 6 inches long and 5 inches wide
    Ⓒ 10 inches long and 3 inches wide
    Ⓓ 15 inches long and 15 inches wide

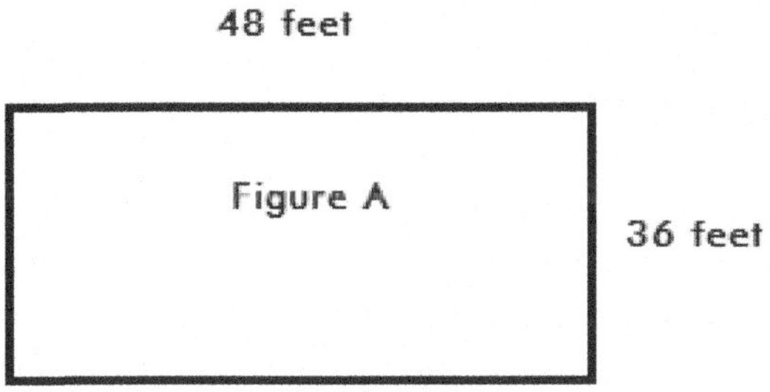

    48 feet

    ┌─────────────────────────────┐
    │   │
    │   Figure A   │ 36 feet
    │   │
    └─────────────────────────────┘

3. **Which of these expressions could be used to find the perimeter of the above figure?**

    Ⓐ 48 + 36 + 2
    Ⓑ 48 x 36
    Ⓒ 2 x (48 + 36)
    Ⓓ 48 + 36

4. **A chalkboard is 72 inches long and 30 inches wide. What is its perimeter?**

    Ⓐ 204 inches
    Ⓑ 2,160 inches
    Ⓒ 102 inches
    Ⓓ 2,100 inches

5. Which of the following statements is true?

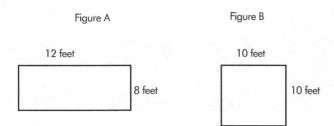

Figure A   Figure B

12 feet   10 feet

8 feet   10 feet

- Ⓐ The two shapes have the same perimeter.
- Ⓑ The two shapes have the same area.
- Ⓒ The two figures are congruent.
- Ⓓ Figure A has a greater area than Figure B.

6. If a square has a perimeter of 100 units, how long is each of its sides?

- Ⓐ 10 units
- Ⓑ 20 units
- Ⓒ 25 units
- Ⓓ Not enough information is given.

7. Find the perimeter of Shape C.

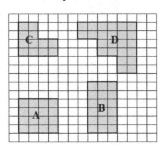

☐ = 1 square unit

- Ⓐ 8 units
- Ⓑ 12 units
- Ⓒ 14 units
- Ⓓ 16 units

8. **Find the area of shape C in square units**

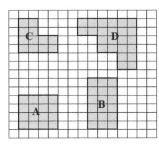

    ☐ = 1 square unit

    Ⓐ 8 square units
    Ⓑ 12 square units
    Ⓒ 14 square units
    Ⓓ 16 square units

9. **What is the perimeter of this shape?**

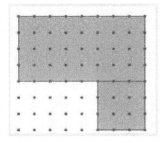

    Ⓐ 24 units
    Ⓑ 28 units
    Ⓒ 30 units
    Ⓓ 34 units

10. **A rectangle has an area of 48 square units and a perimeter of 32 units. What are its dimensions?**

    Ⓐ 6 units by 8 units
    Ⓑ 12 units by 4 units
    Ⓒ 16 units by 3 units
    Ⓓ All of the above are possible.

Chapter 3

Lesson 3: Volume and Cubic Units

1. Which type of unit might be used to record the volume of a rectangular prism?

   (A) inches
   (B) square inches
   (C) ounces
   (D) cubic inches

2. Maeve needed to pack a crate that measured 4 ft. by 2 ft. by 3 ft. with 1 foot cubes. How many 1 foot cubes can she fit in the crate?

3. Complete the following:
   A cereal box has a volume of about _____ .

   (A) 3.0 cubic inches
   (B) 3,000 cubic inches
   (C) 30 cubic inches
   (D) 300 cubic inches

4. Tony and Yolani are measuring the volume of a supply box at school. Tony uses a ruler to measure the box's length, width, and height in centimeters; then he multiplies these measurements. Yolani fills the box with centimeter cubes, then counts the number of cubes. How will their answers compare?

   (A) They cannot be compared because they used different units.
   (B) They will be almost or exactly the same.
   (C) Tony's answer will be greater than Yolani's.
   (D) Yolani's answer will be greater than Tony's.

5. What is the volume of a box that measures 36 in. by 24 in. by 24 in.?

Ⓐ 20,763 cubic inches
Ⓑ 84 cubic inches
Ⓒ 20,736 cubic inches
Ⓓ 111 cubic inches

6. Select the picture that has a volume of 12 cubic units.

Key: 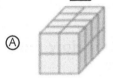 represents one cubic unit

Ⓐ

Ⓑ

Ⓒ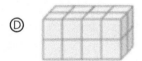

Ⓓ

7. Which of these is an accurate way to measure the volume of a rectangular prism?

Ⓐ Fill it with water and then weigh the water
Ⓑ Trace each face of the prism on centimeter grid paper, and then count the number of squares it comprises
Ⓒ Measure the length and the width, and then multiply the two values
Ⓓ Pack it with unit cubes, leaving no gaps or overlaps, and count the number of unit cubes

8. What is the volume of the rectangular prism? Circle the correct answer choice.

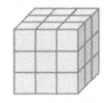 Key: represents one cubic unit

Ⓐ 27 cubic units
Ⓑ 18 cubic units
Ⓒ 16 cubic units
Ⓓ 21 cubic units

9. A container measures 4 inches wide, 6 inches long, and 10 inches high. How many 1 inch cubes will it hold?

Ⓐ 20^2
Ⓑ 240
Ⓒ The cube of 240
Ⓓ Cannot be determined

10. What is the volume of this figure?

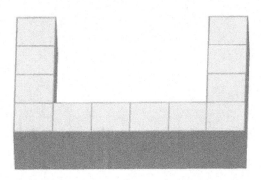 Key: represents one cubic unit

Chapter 3

Lesson 4: Volume of a rectangular prism

1. What is the volume of the figure?

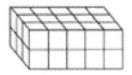

- Ⓐ 60 cubic units
- Ⓑ 15 cubic units
- Ⓒ 30 cubic units
- Ⓓ 31 cubic units

2. What is the volume of the figure?

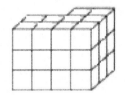

- Ⓐ 30 units³
- Ⓑ 27 units³
- Ⓒ 31 units³
- Ⓓ 36 units³

3. Which of these has a volume of 24 cubic units?

Ⓐ

Ⓑ

Ⓒ

Ⓓ

4. Trevor is building a tower out of centimeter cubes. This is the base of the tower so far.

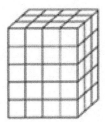

How many more layers must Trevor add to have a tower with a volume of 84 cm³?

5. Kerry built the figure on the left and Milo built the one on the right. If they knock down their two figures to build one large one using all of the blocks, what will its volume be?

 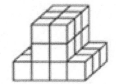

Ⓐ 34 cubic units
Ⓑ 16 cubic units
Ⓒ 52 cubic units
Ⓓ 40 cubic units

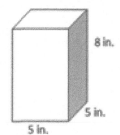

6. What is the volume of the figure in cubic inches?

8 in.

5 in.

5 in.

7. The volume of the figure in _____ cubic cm

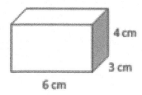

4 cm

3 cm

6 cm

8. The figure has a volume of 66 ft³. What is the height of the figure?

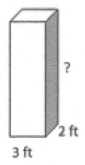

?

2 ft

3 ft

Ⓐ 11 ft
Ⓑ 61 ft
Ⓒ 13 ft
Ⓓ 33 ft

9. The figure has a volume of 14 in³. What is the width of the figure?

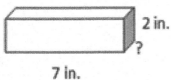

Ⓐ 2 inches
Ⓑ 1 inch
Ⓒ 5 inches
Ⓓ 2.5 inches

10. Which figure has a volume of 42 m³?

Ⓐ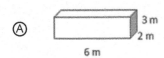

Ⓑ

Ⓒ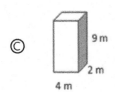

Ⓓ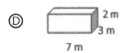

Lesson 5: Coordinate Geometry and Graphing Ordered Pairs of Numbers

1. Assume Point D was added to the grid so that Shape ABCD was a rectangle. Which of these could be the ordered pair for Point D?

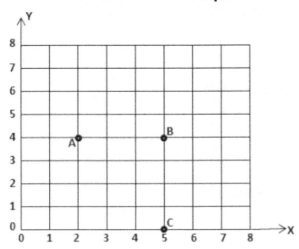

Ⓐ (0, 0)
Ⓑ (0, 2)
Ⓒ (2, 0)
Ⓓ (2, 2)

2. Assume Segments AB and BC were drawn. Compare the lengths of the two segments.

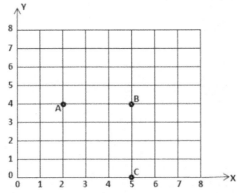

Ⓐ Segment AB is longer than Segment BC.
Ⓑ Segment BC is longer than Segment AB.
Ⓒ Segments AB and BC have the same length.
Ⓓ It cannot be determined from this information.

3.

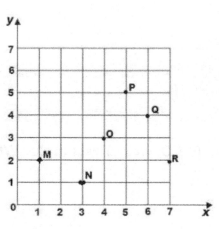

Where is Point R located?

Ⓐ (2, 7)
Ⓑ (7, 2)
Ⓒ (6, 4)
Ⓓ (4, 6)

4. Which point is located at (4, 3)? Explain your answer.

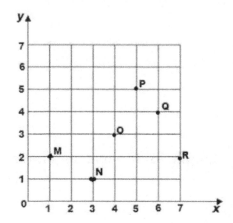

5. Locate Point P on the coordinate grid. Which of the following ordered pairs represents its position?

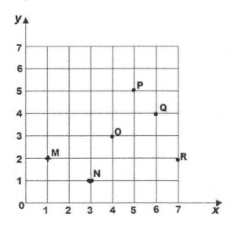

Ⓐ (5, 5)
Ⓑ (3, 1)
Ⓒ (1, 2)
Ⓓ (7, 2)

6. The graph below represents the values listed in the accompanying table, and their linear relationship. Use the graph and the table to respond to the following:
What is the value of c (in the table)?

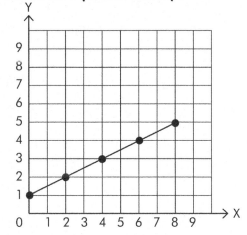

X	Y
0	1
4	a
2	b
8	5
c	4

7. The graph below represents the values listed in the accompanying table, and their linear relationship. Use the graph and the table to respond to the following:
   What is the value of b (in the table)?

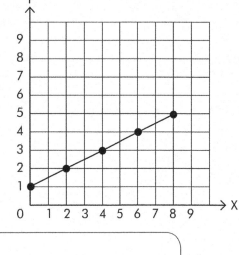

X	Y
0	1
4	a
2	b
8	5
c	4

8. Which of the following graphs best represents the values in this table?

x	y
1	1
2	2
3	3

Ⓐ

Ⓑ

Ⓒ

Ⓓ

9. On a coordinate grid, which of these points would be closest to the origin?

    Ⓐ   (2, 1)
    Ⓑ   (2, 7)
    Ⓒ   (1, 5)
    Ⓓ   (0, 4)

10. If these four ordered pairs (2,4), (5,8), (8,4), (5,0) were plotted to form a diamond, which point would be the top of the diamond?

    Ⓐ   (2, 4)
    Ⓑ   (5, 8)
    Ⓒ   (8, 4)
    Ⓓ   (5, 0)

Lesson 6: Real World Graphing Problems

1. According to the map, what is the location of the weather station (⚡)?

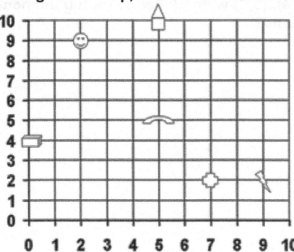

Ⓐ (3,9)
Ⓑ (8,2)
Ⓒ (9,2)
Ⓓ (2,9)

2. According to the map, what is the location of the warehouse (▭)?

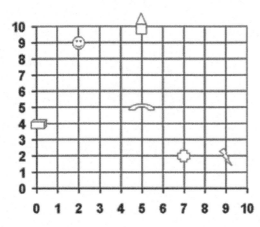

Ⓐ (x = 4)
Ⓑ (0,4)
Ⓒ (y = 4)
Ⓓ (4,0)

3. According to the map, what is located at (7,2)?

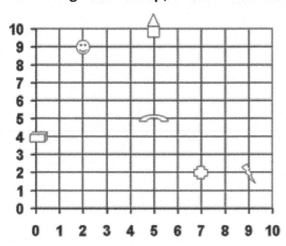

ⓐ   The hospital ⊹

ⓑ   The bridge ⌒

ⓒ   The playground ☺

ⓓ   The house ⌂

4. According to the map, what is located at (5,5)?

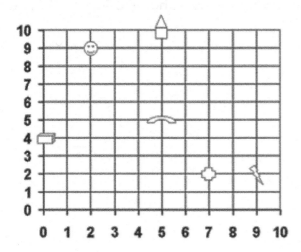

ⓐ   The hospital ⊹

ⓑ   The bridge ⌒

ⓒ   The playground ☺

ⓓ   The house ⌂

5. Which set of directions would lead a person from the playground (🙂) to the hospital (✚)?

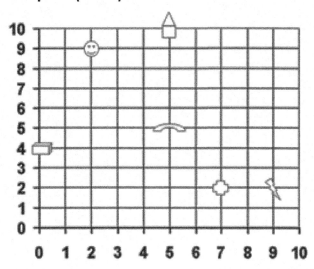

   Ⓐ   Walk 5 units along -ve y-axis and 7 units along +ve x-axis.
   Ⓑ   Walk 7 units along -ve y-axis and 2 units along +ve x-axis.
   Ⓒ   Walk 2 units along -ve y-axis and 7 units along +ve x-axis.
   Ⓓ   Walk 7 units along -ve y-axis and 5 units along +ve x-axis.

6. Which set of directions would lead a person from the weather station (⚡) to the bridge (⌒)?

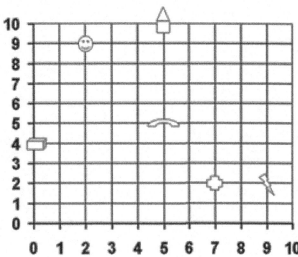

   Ⓐ   Walk 5 units along -ve x-axis and 5 units along +ve y-axis.
   Ⓑ   Walk 2 units along -ve x-axis and 0 units along +ve y-axis.
   Ⓒ   Walk 4 units along -ve x-axis and 3 units along +ve y-axis.
   Ⓓ   Walk 3 units along -ve x-axis and 4 units along +ve y-axis.

7. Where should the town locate a new lumber mill so it is as close as possible to both the warehouse (☐) and the hospital (✛)?

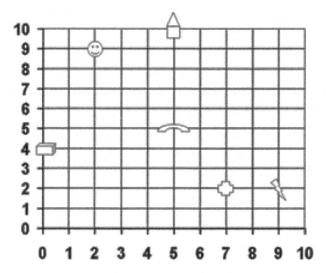

Ⓐ (7,0)
Ⓑ (5,3)
Ⓒ (1,7)
Ⓓ (5,0)

8. According to the map, what is the location of the zebras (🦓)?

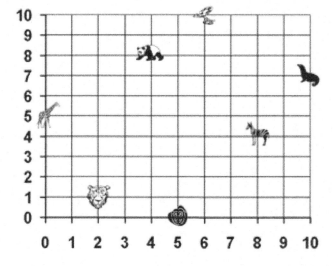

Ⓐ (8,4)
Ⓑ (8,0)
Ⓒ (4,8)
Ⓓ (4,4)

9. According to the map, what is the location of the giraffes (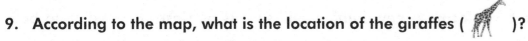)?

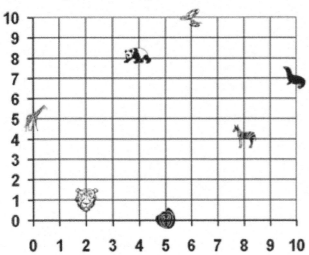

Ⓐ (y = 5)
Ⓑ (0,5)
Ⓒ (x = 5)
Ⓓ (5,0)

10. According to the map, which is located at (10,7)?

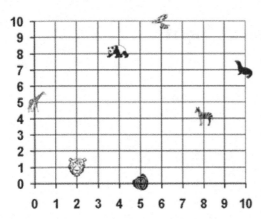

Ⓐ The tigers

Ⓑ The pandas

Ⓒ The snakes

Ⓓ The seals

End of Geometry and Measurment

Answer Key and Detailed Explanations

Chapter 3:
Geometry and Measurement

Lesson 1: Real World Problems with Volume

Question No.	Answer	Detailed Explanations
1	B	A box that holds 54 one feet cubes has a volume of 54 ft^3. To find the box with this volume, multiply the length x width x height (3 x 2 x 9 = 54).
2	150	The number of 1 inch cubes it can hold is equal to its volume in inches^3. To find the volume of the container, multiply the area of the base (30) by its height (5). 30 x 5 = 150.
3	12 cm	The volume of the container (300 cm^3) is equal to the area of the base (25) times its height. Therefore, 300 = 25 x 12.
4	C	To find the volume of a rectangular prism, multiply the length x width x height (12 x 5 x 5 = 300). This is greater than the other three jewelry boxes: 10 x 7 x 4 = 280 8 x 5 x 5 = 200 14 x 2 x 10 = 280
5	20 ft	The volume of the cabinet (20 ft^3) will be equal to the area of the base (4 x 1 = 4) times its height. Therefore, the height should be 5 ft (20 = 4 x 5).
6	B	To determine the amount of soil Bethany would need, find the volume of the garden. Volume = l x w x h = 32 x 14 x 2 = 896 in^3.
7	B	To find the height of the building, use the formula, Volume(V)=Area of the (B) x height(h) V= Bh 1520 = 95h $h = \dfrac{1520}{95} = 16$ feet
8	B	Volume is given by l x 4 x 3 = 36 $L = \dfrac{36}{4 \times 3}$ Here, l = 3 cms. The correct answer is B.
9	C	Volume is given by = 4 x 3 x 5 = 60 cubic feet. Hence, the correct answer is C.
10	D	Volume occupied is given by 2 x 1 x 2 x 15 = 60 cubic meters. Hence, correct answer choice is D.

Lesson 2: Perimeter & Area

Question No.	Answer	Detailed Explanation
1	B	The formula for finding the area of a rectangle: Area = length x width.
2	A	The formula to find the perimeter of a rectangle: P = 2(length) + 2(width)
3	C	The length is 36 ft. and the the width is 48 ft.. All sides must be added to determine the perimeter. Add 48 + 36. Then multiply the sum by 2.
4	A	For the perimeter, add the measurements of the length and width: 72 + 30. Multiply the sum by 2.
5	A	Add the measurement of the length and the width, then multiply the sum by 2. Do this for both figures and compare the perimeters.
6	10 units	The perimeter is the sum of all 4 sides. If that sum is 100, divide 100 by 4 to determine the length of each side. (A square has 4 equal sides.)
7	16 units	To find the perimeter of a shape on the graph sheet, count each side of the squares all the way around the outside of the shape. The side of each square that makes up the shape is a unit.
8	12 square units	To find the area of a shape on the graph sheet, count the number of squares on the inside of the shape.
9	C	Count the segments between the red dots, all the way around the shape.
10	B	Although all three of the choices offered would have an area of 48 square units, only a 12 by 4 rectangle would have a perimeter of 32 units.

Lesson 3: Volume and Cubic Units

Question No.	Answer	Detailed Explanations
1	D	To find the volume of a rectangular solid, multiply the area of the base (l x w) by the height (h). Therefore, the units are cubic units of length, such as cubic inches.
2	24	To find the volume of a rectangular solid, multiply the area of the base (l x w) by the height (h). In this problem, 4 x 2 x 3 = 24 cubic feet. Therefore, it will take 24 cubes to fill the crate, since each cube is one cubic foot.
3	D	One cubic inch is roughly the size of a die. The best estimate for the number of cubic inches it would take to fill a regular cereal box is about 300. The actual volume of a cereal box can be found by multiplying its length x width x height, so an estimate of 10 x 2 x 15 inches is reasonable.
4	B	The formula for determining volume is l x w x h. It can also be determined by counting the number of unit cubes that fill a solid figure. Since Tony and Yolani both used centimeters as their units, their two methods should give them almost the same answer.
5	C	To find the volume of a solid multiply the area of the base (l x w) by the height (h). In this problem, 36 x 24 x 24 = 20,736 cubic inches.
6	B	Count the number of cubes. The picture with 12 cubes has a volume of 12 cubic units. The first picture has 16 cubes, the second 12, the third 8 and the fourth 16.
7	A	To determine the volume of the rectangular prism, count the number of cubes. Each layer has 9 cubes and there are three layers so 9 X 3 = 27 cubes. The volume of the prism is 27 cubic units, choice A.
8	A	To determine the volume of the rectangular prism, count the number of cubes. Each layer has 9 cubes and there are three layers so 9 X 3 = 27 cubes. The volume of the prism is 27 cubic units, choice A.
9	B	The volume of the container is 240 in^3 (4 x 6 x 10). That means it can hold 240 1-inch cubes.
10	12	Count each of the squares as 1 cube, we get total of 12, hence, the correct answer choice is 12.

Lesson 4: Volume of a rectangular prism

Question No.	Answer	Detailed Explanations
1	C	The figure clearly has 15 cubes in the top layer, so there must be another 15 cubes in the bottom layer (the figure is only 2 units high, or 2 layers). Therefore, it has a volume of 30 cubic units (15 + 15 = 30).
2	A	By counting the number of cubes in the figure, you can find that the volume is 30 units^3. There are 3 layers of 8 cubes each in the front part of the figure (3 x 8 = 24) and 3 layers of 2 cubes each at the back of the figure (3 x 2 = 6). Therefore, 24 + 6 = 30.
3	D	By counting the number of cubes in the figure, you can find that the volume is 24 units^3. The bottom layer is 4 by 3 units, so it has a volume of 12 units^3. Each of the top 2 layers is 2 by 3 units, so they each have a volume of 6 units^3. Therefore, 12 + 6 + 6 = 24 units^3.
4	2	The base of the tower measures 4 x 3 x 5, which gives it a volume of 60 cm^3. Since each layer is 4 x 3, it has a volume of 12 cm^3. In order to reach 84 cm^3, Trevor must add 2 more layers (2 x 12 = 24 and 24 + 60 = 84).
5	D	Kerry's figure has a volume of 16 cubic units (you can see 8 cubes at the front of the figure and there are another 8 behind). Trevor's figure has a volume of 24 cubic units (The bottom layer is 4 by 3 units, so it has a volume of 12 units^3. Each of the top 2 layers is 2 by 3 units, so they each have a volume of 6 units^3. Therefore, the volume of Milo's figure is 12 + 6 + 6 = 24 units^3.) Together, their tower's volume is 40 cubic units (16 + 24 = 40).
6	200	To find the volume of a rectangular prism, multiply the length x width x height (5 x 5 x 8 = 200).
7	72	To find the volume of a rectangular prism, multiply the length x width x height (6 x 3 x 4 = 72).
8	A	Since the volume (66 ft^3) must equal length x width x height, then 2 x 3 x 11 = 66.
9	B	Since the volume (14 in^3) must equal length x width x height, then 7 x 1 x 2 = 14.
10	D	To find the volume of a rectangular prism, multiply the length x width x height (7 x 3 x 2 = 42).

Lesson 5: Coordinate Geometry and Graphing Ordered Pairs of Numbers

Question No.	Answer	Detailed Explanations
1	C	A rectangle must have two pairs of parallel sides, so point D must be at 2 on the x-axis (in line with point A) and at 0 on the y-axis (in line with point C).
2	B	Segment AB (from 2 to 5) is 3 units long. Segment BC (from 0 to 4) is 4 units long. Segment BC is longer.
3	B	Using the labels, follow the x-axis as far as point R (7 units) and the y-axis as far as point R (2 units). This makes the coordinate pair (7, 2).
4	Point O	To find point (4, 3), follow the x-axis horizontally 4 units, then follow the y-axis vertically 3 units. The result is point O.
5	A	Using the labels, follow the x-axis as far as point P (5 units) and the y-axis as far as point P (5 units). This makes the coordinate pair (5, 5).
6	6	The coordinate pair is (c, 4), so follow the line on the graph to where its value for y is 4. Follow that point down to the x-axis to see it is 6.
7	2	The coordinate pair is (2, b), so follow the line on the graph to where its value for x is 2. Follow that point across to the y-axis to see it is 2.
8	B	As the value of x increases, the value of y increases equally. This produces an upward-sloping straight line.
9	A	The origin is point (0, 0). The point closest to this would have the lowest x- and y- values (without being negative numbers).
10	B	The points would create this diamond: The top of the diamond is point (5, 8).

Lesson 6: Real world graphing problems

Question No.	Answer	Detailed Explanations
1	C	The location of the weather station is at the intersection of 9 on the x-axis and 2 on the y-axis. Therefore, its coordinates are (9,2).
2	B	The location of the warehouse is at the intersection of 0 on the x-axis and 4 on the y-axis. Therefore, its coordinates are (0,4).
3	A	At the intersection of 7 on the x-axis and 2 on the y-axis, the hospital is located.
4	B	At the intersection of 5 on the x-axis and 5 on the y-axis, the bridge is located.
5	D	Starting at the playground (2,9), walking 7 units along the -ve y-axis could bring a person to (2,2). From there, walking 5 units along the +ve x-axis could bring that person to (7,2), to the location of the hospital.
6	C	Starting at the weather station (9,2), walking 4 units along the -ve x-axis could bring a person to (5,2). From there, walking 3 units along the +ve y-axis could bring that person to (5,5), to the location of the bridge.
7	B	This is the only set of coordinates given that is located between the warehouse and the hospital, making it the closest to both locations.
8	A	The location of the zebras is at the intersection of 8 on the x-axis and 4 on the y-axis. Therefore, its coordinates are (8,4).
9	B	The location of the giraffes is at the intersection of 0 on the x-axis and 5 on the y-axis. Therefore, its coordinates are (0,5).
10	D	At the intersection of 10 on the x-axis and 7 on the y-axis, the seals are located.

Chapter 4:
Data Analysis

Chapter 4

Lesson 1: Representing and Interpreting Data

1. A 5th grade science class is raising mealworms. The students measured the mealworms and recorded the lengths on this line plot.

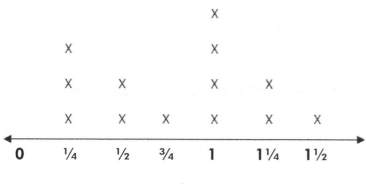

Length of Mealworms

Inches

According to this line plot, what was the length of the longest mealworm?

- Ⓐ $\frac{1}{4}$ inch
- Ⓑ $\frac{3}{4}$ inch
- Ⓒ 1 inch
- Ⓓ $1\frac{1}{2}$ inches

2. A 5th grade science class is raising mealworms. The students measured the mealworms and recorded the lengths on this line plot.

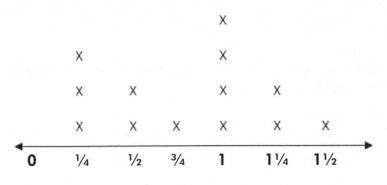

Length of Mealworms

Inches

According to this line plot, what was the length of the shortest mealworm?

Ⓐ $\frac{1}{4}$ inch

Ⓑ $\frac{3}{4}$ inch

Ⓒ $1\frac{1}{4}$ inch

Ⓓ 0

3. A 5th grade science class is raising mealworms. The students measured the mealworms and recorded the lengths on this line plot.

Length of Mealworms

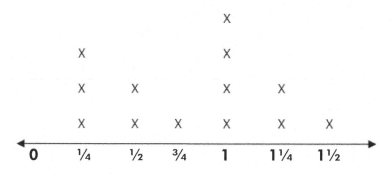

Inches

According to this line plot, what was the most common length for mealworms?

Ⓐ $1\frac{1}{2}$ inches

Ⓑ $\frac{3}{4}$ inch

Ⓒ $\frac{1}{4}$ inch

Ⓓ 1 inch

4. A 5th grade science class is raising mealworms. The students measured the mealworms and recorded the lengths on this line plot.

Length of Mealworms

```
                          X
        X                 X
        X       X         X         X
        X       X    X    X    X    X
   ◄————————————————————————————————————►
   0   ¼      ½   ¾    1   1¼   1½
```

Inches

According to this line plot, how many mealworms were less than 1 inch long?

5. A 5th grade science class is raising mealworms. The students measured the mealworms and recorded the lengths on this line plot.

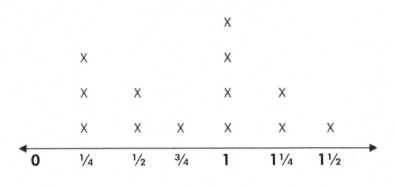

Length of Mealworms

Inches

According to this line plot, how many mealworms were measured in all?

6. A 5th grade science class is raising mealworms. The students measured the mealworms and recorded the lengths on this line plot.

Length of Mealworms

Inches

According to this line plot, what is the median length of a mealworm?

Ⓐ 1 inch
Ⓑ 13 inches
Ⓒ between $\frac{3}{4}$ inch and 1 inch
Ⓓ $1\frac{1}{2}$ inches

7. **A 5th grade science class is raising mealworms. The students measured the mealworms and recorded the lengths on this line plot.**

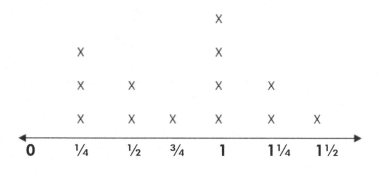

How could someone use this line plot to find the total length of all the mealworms?

Ⓐ Add each of the numbers along the bottom of the line plot
Ⓑ Multiply each of the numbers along the bottom of the line plot
Ⓒ Multiply each length by its number of Xs, then add the values
Ⓓ Multiply each of the numbers along the bottom of the line plot by the total number of Xs, then add the values

8. **A 5th grade science class is raising mealworms. The students measured the mealworms and recorded the lengths on this line plot.**

Length of Mealworms

```
                                X
            X                   X
            X       X           X       X
            X       X   X       X       X       X
    ◄───────────────────────────────────────────►
        0   ¼       ½   ¾   1   1¼      1½
```

Inches

Which of these mealworm lengths would not fit within the range of this line plot?

Ⓐ $\frac{7}{8}$ inch

Ⓑ $1\frac{3}{4}$ inches

Ⓒ $1\frac{1}{8}$ inches

Ⓓ $\frac{5}{16}$ inch

9. A 5th grade science class is observing weather conditions. The students measured the amount of precipitation each day and recorded it on this line plot.

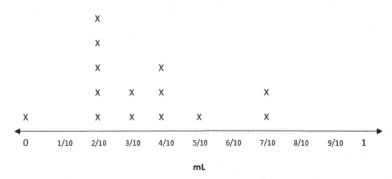

According to this line plot, what was the most precipitation recorded in one day?

Ⓐ $4\frac{7}{10}$ mL

Ⓑ $\frac{7}{10}$ mL

Ⓒ $\frac{9}{10}$ mL

Ⓓ $\frac{2}{10}$ mL

10. A 5th grade science class is observing weather conditions. The students measured the amount of precipitation each day and recorded it on this line plot.

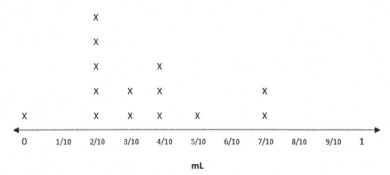

According to this line plot, what was the least amount of precipitation that fell on days that had precipitation? Express your answer in ml.

Chapter 4

Lesson 2: Interpreting Data Tables & Scatter Plots

1. If a scatter plot has a line of best fit that decreases from left to right, which of the following terms describes the association?

Ⓐ Positive association
Ⓑ Negative association
Ⓒ Constant association
Ⓓ Nonlinear association

2. If a scatter plot has a line of best fit that increases from left to right, which of the following terms describes the association?

Ⓐ Positive association
Ⓑ Negative association
Ⓒ Constant association
Ⓓ Nonlinear association

3. Which of the following scatter plots is the best example of a linear association?

Ⓐ

Ⓒ

Ⓑ

Ⓓ

4. Data for 9 kids' History and English grades are made available in the chart. What is the association between the History and English grades?

Kids	1	2	3	4	5	6	7	8	9
History	63	49	84	33	55	23	71	62	41
English	67	69	82	32	59	26	73	62	39

Ⓐ Positive association
Ⓑ Negative association
Ⓒ Nonlinear association
Ⓓ Constant association

5. Data for 9 kids' History grades and the distance they live from school are made available in the chart. What is the association between these two categories?

Kids	1	2	3	4	5	6	7	8	9
History	63	49	84	33	55	23	71	62	41
Distance from School (miles)	.5	7	3	4	5	2	3	6	9

Ⓐ No association
Ⓑ Positive association
Ⓒ Negative association
Ⓓ Constant association

6. 150 students were surveyed and asked whether they played a sport and whether they played a musical instrument. The results are shown in the table below.

	Plays an Instrument	Does not Plays an Instrument
Plays a Sport	60	30
Does not Plays a Sport	10	50

What fraction of the students play an instrument but do not play a sport?

7. Which of the scatter plots below is the best example of positive association?

Ⓐ

Ⓑ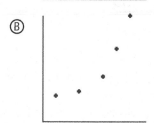

Ⓒ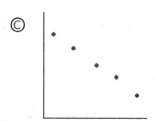

Ⓓ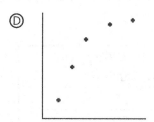

8. 150 students were surveyed and asked whether they played a sport and whether they played a musical instrument. The results are shown in the table below.

	Plays an Instrument	Does not Plays an Instrument
Plays a Sport	60	30
Does not Plays a Sport	10	50

What percent of the 150 students play a sport but do not play an instrument?

9. 150 students were surveyed and asked whether they played a sport and whether they played a musical instrument. The results are shown in the table below.

	Plays an Instrument	Does not Plays an Instrument
Plays a Sport	60	30
Does not Plays a Sport	10	50

Which of the following statements is NOT supported by the data?

Ⓐ   A randomly chosen student who plays a sport is 2 times as likely to play an instrument as to not play an instrument.

Ⓑ   A randomly chosen student who does not play an instrument is 2 times as likely to not play a sport as to play a sport.

Ⓒ   A randomly chosen student who does not play a sport is 5 times as likely to not play an instrument as to play an instrument.

Ⓓ   A randomly chosen student who plays an instrument is 6 times as likely to play a sport as to not play a sport.

10. 150 students were surveyed and asked whether they played a sport and whether they played a musical instrument. The results are shown in the table below.

	Plays an Instrument	Does not Plays an Instrument
Plays a Sport	60	30
Does not Plays a Sport	10	50

Which two sections add up to just over half of the number of students surveyed?

Ⓐ The two sections that do not play an instrument.
Ⓑ The two sections that do not play a sport.
Ⓒ The two sections that play an instrument.
Ⓓ The two sections that play a sport.

End of Data Analysis

Answer Key and Detailed Explanations

Chapter 4: Data Analysis

Lesson 1: Representing and Interpreting Data

Question No.	Answer	Detailed Explanations
1	D	The length of each mealworm is shown along the bottom of the line plot. The highest value on the scale is $1\frac{1}{2}$ inches and the Xs above show that there were mealworms this long.
2	A	The length of each mealworm is shown along the bottom of the line plot. The lowest value on the scale is $\frac{1}{4}$ inch and the Xs above show that there were mealworms this long.
3	D	The Xs on the line plot represent the number of mealworms at each length. Since 1 inch has the most Xs above it (4), it is the most common length.
4	6	The Xs on the line plot represent the number of mealworms at each length. There were 3 mealworms that were $\frac{1}{4}$ inch long, 2 that were $\frac{1}{2}$ inch long, and 1 that was $\frac{3}{4}$ inch long. Altogether, that's 6 mealworms that are less than 1 inch long.
5	13	The Xs on the line plot represent the number of mealworms at each length. There are 13 Xs in all, at various lengths.
6	C	**Rule:** If the number data are odd, there will be one middle number which will be the median. If the number of data are even, there will be two middle numbers and the average of these numbers gives the median of the data set. Since the number of mealworms is 13, which is an odd number, there will be one middle value i.e. (13+1)/2 = 7th value. 7th mealworm's length is 1inch therefore the median length of the mealworms is 1inch.
7	C	To find the total length, you would have to add together the three mealworms that are $\frac{1}{4}$ inch long (3 x $\frac{1}{4}$) plus the two that are $\frac{1}{2}$ inch long (2 x $\frac{1}{2}$) and so on for each length.
8	B	$1\frac{3}{4}$ inches is greater than $1\frac{1}{2}$ inches, so it would not fall within the range of $\frac{1}{4}$ to $1\frac{1}{2}$ inches.
9	B	The amount of precipitation each day is shown along the bottom of the line plot. The highest value on the scale that has Xs above it, showing that there was a day that received that amount, is $\frac{7}{10}$ mL.

Question No.	Answer	Detailed Explanations
10	$\frac{2}{10}$ mL	The amount of precipitation each day is shown along the bottom of the line plot. The lowest value on the scale other than zero that has Xs above it is $\frac{2}{10}$ mL.

Lesson 2: Interpreting Data Tables & Scatter Plots

Question No.	Answer	Detailed Explanations
1	B	By definition, a decreasing trend from left to right on a scatter plot indicates a negative association.
2	A	By definition, an increasing line from left to right on a scatter plot indicates a positive association.
3	C	The points in the third choice are nearly in a straight line.
4	A	As the History grade increases, so does the English grade. Thus, there is a positive association.
5	A	There does not appear to be any significant correlation between these two variables.
6	$\frac{1}{7}$	70 play an instrument. Of those 10 do not play a sport; so $\frac{10}{70} = \frac{1}{7}$
7	A	In the first graph, a best fit line would be nearly a straight line increasing to the right.
8	20%	$\frac{30}{150} \times 100$ = 20%
9	B	Option (B) is the correct answer. 80 do not play an instrument and 50 of those do not play a sport. Among these 80 students, ratio of those who do no play a sport to those who play a sport is 50:30 = 5:3, It is not 2:1 as given in the option (B). All the other statements are supported by the data.
10	A	30+50=80, which is about half of 150.

Additional Information

Test Taking Tips

1) **The day before the test,** make sure you get a good night's sleep.

2) **On the day of the test,** be sure to eat a good hearty breakfast! Also, be sure to arrive at school on time.

3) **During the test:**

- **Read every question carefully.**

  - Do not spend too much time on any one question. Work steadily through all questions in the section.
  - Attempt all of the questions even if you are not sure of some answers.
  - If you run into a difficult question, eliminate as many choices as you can and then pick the best one from the remaining choices. Intelligent guessing will help you increase your score.
  - Also, mark the question so that if you have extra time, you can return to it after you reach the end of the section.
  - Some questions may refer to a graph, chart, or other kind of picture. Carefully review the graphic before answering the question.
  - Be sure to include explanations for your written responses and show all work.

- **While Answering Multiple-Choice questions.**

  - Read the question completely.
  - Go through the answer choices.
  - If you are struggling with picking out a correct answer, it is best to eliminate some of the choices. At least try to eliminate two of the choices.
  - Reread the question and find support from the passage to support one of the answers.
  - Recheck the question and your answer.

Note: The Texas STAAR Redesign Math assessments also includes Grid In type questions in the pencil and paper version of the test.

Frequently Asked Questions(FAQs)

For more information on Assessment Year, visit
www.lumoslearning.com/a/staar-faqs
OR Scan the **QR Code**

Step 1 → **Visit the link given below and login to your parent/teacher account**

www.lumoslearning.com

Step 2 → <u>**For Parent**</u>

Click on the horizontal lines (☰) in the top right-hand corner and select **"My tedBooks"**. Place the Book Access Code and submit.

<u>**For Teacher**</u>

Click on "My Subscription" under the "My Account" menu in the left-hand side and select **"My tedBooks"**. Place the Book Access Code and submit.

Note: See the first page for access code.

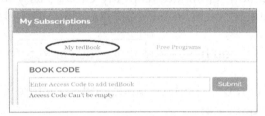

Step 3 → **Add the new book**

To add the new book for a registered student, choose the '**Student**' button and click on submit.

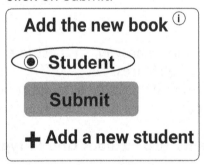

To add the new book for a new student, choose the '**Add New Student**' button and complete the student registration.

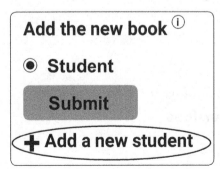

Progress Chart

Standard	Lesson	Score	Date of Completion
TEKS			
5.2 (A)	Read and write decimals		
5.2 (B)	Comparing and Ordering Decimals		
5.2 (C)	Rounding Decimals		
5.3 (A)	Record and interpret calculations with numbers		
5.3 (B)	Multiplication of whole numbers		
5.3 (C)	Division of whole numbers		
5.3(D) 5.3 (E)	Multiply Decimals		
5.3 (F) 5.3 (G)	Divide Decimals		
5.3 (H)	Add & Subtract Fractions		
5.3 (H)	Problem Solving with Fractions		
5.3 (I)	Multiply Fractions		
5.3 (I)	Real world problems with Fractions		
5.3 (J)	Dividing by unit fractions		
5.3 (K)	Rational Numbers, Addition & Subtraction		
5.3 (L)	Divide whole numbers by unit fractions and unit fractions by whole numbers.		
5.4 (A)	Identify prime and composite numbers		
5.4 (B)	Solve multi-step problems involving the four operations		
5.4 (C) 5.4 (D)	Analyze patterns and relationships		
5.4 (E)	Write & Interpret Numerical Expressions & Patterns		
5.4 (G)	Real world problems with volume		
5.4 (H)	Perimeter & Area		
5.6 (A)	Volume and Cubic Units		
5.6 (B)	Volume of a rectangular prism		
5.8 (A)	Coordinate Geometry and Graphing Ordered Pairs of Numbers		
5.8 (C)	Real world graphing problems		
5.9 (A) 5.9 (C)	Representing and Interpreting Data		
5.9 (B)	Interpreting Data Tables & Scatter Plots		

Grade **5**

Lumos Learning
Step Up Your Skills

TEXAS
ENGLISH
LANGUAGE ARTS LITERACY
STAAR Practice

Revised Edition

(((tedBook)))
ONLINE

2 Practice Tests

Personalized Study Plan

Available

• At Leading book stores

• Online www.LumosLearning.com

Made in the USA
Coppell, TX
15 April 2024

31297653R00083